SAFETY

IN ACADEMIC
CHEMISTRY
LABORATORIES

A PUBLICATION OF
THE AMERICAN CHEMICAL SOCIETY
COMMITTEE ON CHEMICAL SAFETY
FIFTH EDITION

i

Preface

This is the fifth edition of the Academic Safety Manual which was first published in 1970 by the American Chemical Society Committee on Chemical Safety. During the past twenty years, many thousands of students and faculty have used the materials presented to develop their own safety programs.

The production of the manual has always been a Committee effort. However, a small group of the members of the Committee on Chemical Safety has been responsible for the actual collection of the information as well as the writing of the text. Warren Smith served as the chairman of this fifth edition project. He was generously supported by Committee members and friends, Richard Bayer, Donald Clemens, Carl Gottschall, Daniel Liberman, Stanley Pine, Patricia Redden, Elizabeth Weisburger and Jay Young. Maureen Matkovich, the Committee liaison, provided valuable technical assistance.

All comments are welcome. Please direct them to the Committee on Chemical Safety, American Chemical Society, 1155 Sixteenth Street, NW, Washington, DC 20036.

> Stanley H. Pine
> Chairman, ACS Committee
> on Chemical Safety

Disclaimer

The materials contained in this manual have been compiled by recognized authorities from sources believed to be reliable and to represent the best opinions on the subject. This manual is intended to serve only as a starting point for good practices and does not purport to specify minimal legal standards or to represent the policy of the American Chemical Society. No warranty, guarantee, or representation is made by the American Chemical Society as to the accuracy or sufficiency of the information contained herein, and the Society assumes no responsibility in connection therewith. This manual is intended to provide basic guidelines for safe practices. Therefore, it cannot be assumed that all necessary warning and precautionary measures are contained in this document and that other or additional information or measures may not be required. Users of this manual should consult pertinent local, state and federal laws and legal counsel prior to initiating any safety program.

Registered names and trademarks, etc., used in this publication, even without specific indication thereof, are not to be considered unprotected by law.

Table of Contents

Introduction

The American Chemical Society Committee on Chemical Safety has prepared these guidelines for prudent practice in academic chemistry laboratories. The guidelines can be adapted to practices in all laboratories using chemicals, including research, clinical, quality control, and development laboratories, as well as in other workplaces using chemicals. These general recommendations can serve as a basis for more detailed instructions prepared for each chemical laboratory by those directly responsible.

There is a preferred way to perform all work with chemicals which can both reduce the probability of an accident to a negligible level and reduce its consequences to minimal levels should one occur. Risk minimization depends upon safe laboratory practices, appropriate engineering controls for chemical containment, the proper use of personal protective equipment, the use of the least quantity of material necessary to demonstrate the principle of the experiment, and, when possible, the substitution of a less hazardous chemical for a more hazardous one. Before beginning an operation or performing an experiment, ask "What would happen if...?" Answers to this question require an understanding of the hazards associated with the chemicals and equipment involved. The reactivity, flammability, corrosivity and toxicity of chemicals used will dictate the precautions to be taken. Such precautionary information might well form an introductory section to all written procedures.

Prudent practice requires an effective safety program. An effective safety program must have strong support from the top administrative officer and will actively involve faculty, staff and students. Without the direct and enthusiastic support of the top administrative officer, who is ultimately responsible for safety within any facility, an effective safety program is rarely achieved. A safety officer, appropriately trained and qualified, is essential. However, even the best safety officer cannot relieve the head of the laboratory, the faculty and the students of their responsibility for the safety of operations under their jurisdiction. A good safety program includes constant training and reminders of the common hazards to which laboratory workers may be exposed as well as attention to the materials, equipment and facilities with which they work. The rapid accumulation of new information and changing regulations demand special attention to the training of experienced laboratory workers whose knowledge and habits may not appropriately reflect the current state of prudent practices.

Good practice needs mandatory safety rules and programs. To achieve safe conditions for students and other laboratory workers, the program must include regular safety inspections at intervals of no more than three months (and at shorter intervals for certain types of equipment, such as safety showers and eyewash fountains), disposal procedures that ensure proper disposal of waste chemicals at regular intervals, formal and regular safety programs to ensure that sufficient full-time personnel are trained in the proper use of emergency equipment and procedures, and regular monitoring of the performance of equipment and ventilation systems.

This manual is primarily for students in chemistry laboratories, but the chemistry faculty who develop and oversee the laboratory programs are not forgotten. The latter part of this manual summarizes many of the aspects of laboratory safety from the administrative viewpoint, including consideration of the many regulations developed under the Resource Conservation and Recovery Act (RCRA) and the Occupational Safety and Health Act. However, the reason for making safety an integral part of all laboratory operations is not the regulations and their associated legal implications, but rather that doing things safely is the right way to work.

Safety in Academic Chemistry Laboratories provides a starting point for understanding good laboratory practices. Some of the information presented here has been derived from regulatory sources, but most of the material is the result of the many years of practical knowledge of the members of the Committee on Chemical Safety. The manual is not intended to establish universal rules or regulations. It will, however, provide a solid basis from which individual safety procedures can be developed.

Student laboratory guide

Section I
Personal Protection and Laboratory Protocol

Safety is a collective responsibility that requires the full cooperation of everyone in the laboratory. However, the ultimate responsibility for safety rests with the person actually carrying out some type of procedure. In the case of an academic laboratory, that is usually the student. Accidents often result from an indifferent attitude, failure to use common sense, or failure to follow instructions. Each student should be aware of what the other students are doing because all can be victims of one individual's mistake. Do not hesitate to point out to other students that they are engaging in unsafe practices or operations. If necessary, report it to the instructor. In the final assessment, students have the greatest responsibility to ensure their own personal safety.

This guide provides a list of do's and don'ts to minimize safety and health problems associated with experimental laboratory work. The manual also provides, where possible, the ideas and concepts which underlie the practical suggestions. However, the reader is expected to become involved and to contribute to the overall solutions. The following are general guidelines for all laboratory workers:

(a) Follow all safety instructions carefully.
(b) Become thoroughly acquainted with the location and use of safety facilities such as safety showers, exits and eyewash fountains.
(c) Become familiar with the hazards of the chemicals being used, and know the safety precautions and emergency procedures before undertaking any work.
(d) Become familiar with the chemical operations and the hazards involved before beginning an operation.

1. Personal Protection
1.1 Eye Protection
All people in the laboratory including visitors must wear eye protection at all times, even when not performing a chemical operation. Wearing of contact lenses in the laboratory is normally forbidden because contact lenses can hold foreign materials against the cornea. Furthermore, they may be difficult to remove in the case of a splash. Soft contact lenses present a particular hazard because they can absorb and retain chemical vapors. If the use of contact lenses is required for therapeutic reasons, fitted goggles must also be worn. In addition, approved standing shields and face shields that protect the neck and ears as well as the face should be available when appropriate for work at reduced pressure or where there is a potential for explosions, implosions or splashing. Normal prescription eyeglasses, though meeting the Food and Drug Administration's standards for shatter resistance, do not provide appropriate laboratory eye protection.

3

1.2 Clothing

Clothing worn in the laboratory should offer protection from splashes and spills, should be easily removable in case of accident, and should be at least fire resistant. Nonflammable, nonporous aprons offer the most satisfactory and the least expensive protection. Lab jackets or coats should have snap fasteners rather than buttons so that they can be readily removed. For further information, see Appendix I.

High-heeled or open-toed shoes, sandals, or shoes made of woven material should not be worn in the laboratory. Shorts, cutoffs and miniskirts are also inappropriate. Long hair and loose clothing should be constrained. Jewelry such as rings, bracelets, and watches should not be worn in order to prevent chemical seepage under the jewelry, contact with electrical sources, catching on equipment, and damage to the jewelry itself.

1.3 Gloves

Gloves can serve as an important part of personal protection when they are used correctly. Check to ensure the absence of cracks or small holes in the gloves before each use. In order to prevent the unintentional spread of chemicals, gloves should be removed before leaving the work area and before handling such things as telephones, doorknobs, writing instruments, and laboratory notebooks. Gloves may be reused, cleaned, or discarded, consistent with their use and contamination.

A wide variety of gloves is available to protect against chemical exposure. Because the permeability of gloves of the same or similar material varies from manufacturer to manufacturer, no specific recommendations are given here. Be aware that if a chemical diffuses through a glove, that chemical is held against the worker's hand and the individual may then be more exposed to the chemical than if the glove had not been worn.

1.4 Personal Hygiene

Everyone working in a chemistry laboratory should be aware of the dangers of ingesting chemicals. These common sense precautions will minimize the possibility of such exposure:

(a) Do not prepare, store (even temporarily), or consume food or beverages in any chemical laboratory.
(b) Do not smoke in any chemical laboratory. Additionally, be aware that tobacco products in opened packages can absorb chemical vapors.
(c) Do not apply cosmetics in a laboratory.
(d) Wash hands and arms thoroughly before leaving the laboratory, even if gloves have been worn.
(e) Wash separately from personal laundry, lab coats or jackets on which chemicals have been spilled.
(f) Never wear or bring lab coats or jackets into areas where food is consumed.
(g) Never pipette by mouth. Always use a pipette aid or suction bulb.

2. Laboratory Protocol

The chemistry laboratory is a place for serious learning and working. Horseplay cannot be tolerated. Variations in procedures including changes in quantities or reagents may be dangerous. Such alterations may only be made with the knowledge and approval of the instructor.

2.1 Housekeeping
In the laboratory and elsewhere, keeping things clean and neat generally leads to a safer environment. Avoid unnecessary hazards by keeping drawers and cabinets closed while working. Never store materials, especially chemicals, on the floor, even temporarily. Work spaces and storage areas should be kept clear of broken glassware, leftover chemicals and scraps of paper. Keep aisles free of obstructions such as chairs, boxes and waste receptacles. Avoid slipping hazards by keeping the floor clear of ice, stoppers, glass beads or rods, other small items, and spilled liquids. Use the required procedure for the proper disposal of chemical wastes and solvents.

2.2 Cleaning Glassware
Clean glassware at the laboratory sink or in laboratory dishwashers. Use hot water, if available, and soap or other detergent. If necessary, use a mild scouring powder. Wear appropriate gloves that have been checked to ensure that no holes are present. Use brushes of suitable stiffness and size. Avoid accumulating too many articles in the cleanup area. Usually work space around a sink is limited and piling up dirty or cleaned glassware leads to breakage. Remember that the turbid water in a sink may hide a jagged edge on a piece of broken glassware that was intact when put into the water. A pair of heavy gloves may be useful for removing broken glass, but care must be exercised to prevent glove contamination. To minimize breakage of glassware, sink bottoms should have rubber or plastic mats which do not block the drains.

Avoid the use of strong cleaning agents such as nitric acid, chromic acid, sulfuric acid, strong oxidizers, or any chemical with a "per" in its name (such as perchloric acid, ammonium persulfate, *etc.*) unless specifically instructed to use them, and then only when wearing proper protective equipment. A number of explosions involving strong oxidizing cleaning solutions, such as chromic sulfuric acid mixtures, have been reported. The use of flammable solvents should be minimized and, when they are used, appropriate precautions must be observed.

2.3 Transporting Chemicals
Transport all chemicals using the container-within-a-container concept. This will shield them from shock during any sudden change of movement. Large containers of corrosives should be transported from central storage in a chemically resistant bucket or other container designed for this purpose. Stairs must be negotiated carefully. Elevators, unless specifically indicated and so designated, should not be used for carrying chemicals. Smoking is never allowed around chemicals and apparatus in transit or in the work area itself.

When moving in the laboratory, anticipate sudden backing up or changes in direction from others. If you stumble or fall while carrying glassware or chemicals, try to project them away from yourself and others.

When a flammable liquid is withdrawn from a drum, or when a drum is filled, both the drum and the other equipment must be electrically wired to each other and to the ground in order to avoid the possible buildup of a static charge. Only small quantities should be transferred to glass containers. If transferring from a metal container to glass, the metal container should be grounded.

2.4 Disposal

The handling of reaction byproducts, surplus and waste chemicals, and contaminated materials is an important part of laboratory safety procedures. Each laboratory worker is responsible for ensuring that wastes are handled in a manner that minimizes personal hazard and recognizes the potential for environmental contamination.

Most instructional laboratories will have clear procedures for students to follow in order to minimize the generation of waste materials. Typically reaction byproducts and surplus chemicals will be neutralized or deactivated as part of the experimental procedure. Waste materials must be handled in specific ways as designated by federal and local regulations.

Some general guidelines are

(a) Dispose of waste materials promptly. When disposing of chemicals one basic principle applies: Keep each different class of chemical in a separate *clearly labeled* disposal container.

(b) Never put chemicals into a sink or down the drain unless they are deactivated or neutralized and they are allowed by local regulation in the sanitary sewer system. Nothing except water or dilute aqueous solutions of non-toxics (e.g., sodium chloride, sugar, soap) from a chemistry laboratory should be disposed of in the sink.

(c) Put ordinary waste paper in a wastepaper basket separate from the chemical wastes. If a piece of paper is contaminated, such as paper toweling used to clean up a spill, put the contaminated paper in the special container that is marked for this use. It must be treated as a chemical waste.

(d) Broken glass belongs in its own marked waste container. Broken thermometers may contain mercury in the fragments and these belong in their own special "broken thermometer" container. See Section III of this manual for instructions on cleaning up mercury spills from broken thermometers.

(e) Peroxides, because of their reactivity, and the unpredictable nature of their formation in laboratory chemicals, have attracted considerable attention. The disposal of large quantities (25 g or more) of peroxides requires expert assistance. For disposal of smaller quantities, see the Overview for Faculty and Administrators. Consider each case individually for handling and disposal.

The Environmental Protection Agency (EPA) classifies wastes by their reaction characteristics. A summary of the major classifications and some general treatment guidelines are listed below. Specific information may be found in the book, *Prudent Practices for Disposal of Chemicals from Laboratories,* as well as other reference materials.

Ignitability: These substances generally include flammable solvents and certain solids. Flammable solvents must never be poured down the drain. They should be collected for disposal in approved flammable solvent containers. In some cases it may be feasible to recover and reuse solvents by distillation. Such solvent recovery must include appropriate safety precautions and attention to potentially dangerous contamination such as that due to peroxide formation.

Corrosivity: This classification includes common acids and bases. They must be collected in waste containers that will not ultimately corrode and leak, such as plastic containers. It often may be appropriate to neutralize waste acids with waste bases and where allowed by local regulations, dispose of the neutral materials via the sanitary sewer system. Again, the nature of the neutralized material must be considered to ensure that it does not involve an environmental hazard such as chromium salts from chromic acid neutralization.

Reactivity: These substances include reactive metals such as sodium and various water reactive reagents. Compounds such as cyanides or sulfides are included in this class if they can readily evolve toxic gases such as hydrogen cyanide. Their collection for disposal must be carried out with particular care. When present in small quantities, it is advisable to deactivate reactive metals by careful reaction with appropriate alcohols and to deactivate certain oxygen or sulfur containing compounds through oxidation. Specific procedures should be consulted.

Toxicity: Although the EPA has specific procedures for determining toxicity, all chemicals may be toxic in certain concentrations. Appropriate procedures should be established in each laboratory for collection and disposal of these materials.

2.5 Unattended Operation of Equipment

Reactions that are left to run unattended overnight or at other times are prime sources for fires, floods and explosions. Do not let equipment such as power stirrers, hot plates, heating mantles, and water condensers run overnight without fail-safe provisions and the instructor's consent. Check unattended reactions periodically. Always leave a note plainly posted with a phone number where you and the instructor can be reached in case of emergency. Remember that in the middle of the night, emergency personnel are entirely dependent on accurate instructions and information.

2.6 Fume Hoods and Ventilation

A large number of common substances present acute respiratory hazards and should not be used in a confined area in large amounts. They should be dispensed and handled only where there is adequate ventilation, such as in a hood. Adequate ventilation is defined as ventilation that is sufficient to keep the concentration of a chemical below the threshold limit value or permissible exposure limit.

If you smell a chemical, it is obvious that you are inhaling it. However, odor does not necessarily indicate that a dangerous concentration has been reached. By contrast, many chemicals can be present at hazardous concentrations without any noticeable odor.

2.7 Refrigerators

Chemicals stored in refrigerators should be sealed, double packaged if possible, and labeled with the name of the material, the date placed in the refrigerator, and the name of the person who stored the material. A current inventory should be maintained. Old chemicals should be disposed of after a specified storage period. Household refrigerators should not be used for chemical storage. See the Overview for Faculty and Administrators.

If used for storage of radioactive materials, a refrigerator should be plainly marked with the standard radioactivity symbol and lettering, and routine surveys should be made to ensure that the radioactive material has not contaminated the refrigerator.

Food should never be stored in a refrigerator used for chemical storage. These refrigerators should be clearly labeled "No Food". Conversely food refrigerators, which must be always outside of, and away from, the chemical work area, should be labeled "Food Only—No Chemicals".

Section II
Recommended Laboratory Techniques

1. General Equipment Setup
1.1 Glassware and Plasticware

Borosilicate glassware is recommended for all laboratory glassware except for special experiments that use UV or other light sources. The only soft glass provided in the laboratory should be reagent bottles, measuring equipment, stirring rods, and tubing.

Any glass equipment to be evacuated, such as suction flasks, should be specially designed with heavy walls. Dewar flasks and large vacuum vessels should be taped or otherwise screened or contained in a metal jacket to prevent flying glass in the case of an implosion. Household Thermos bottles have thin walls and are not acceptable substitutes for laboratory Dewar flasks.

Bottles, jars, and other containers of acids, alkalies, flammable or combustible substances, or corrosive chemicals should be transported in carriers to protect them from breakage, as well as to limit the spread in case of leaks. Note that even plastic containers can break and leak because plastic can be punctured, fail under pressure or heat, or crack through aging.

1.2 Preparation of Glass Tubing and Stoppers

To cut glass tubing, hold the tubing against a firm support and make one quick firm stroke with a sharp triangular file or glass cutter, rocking the file to extend the deep nick one-third around the circumference. Cover the tubing with cloth and hold the tubing in both hands, away from the body. Place the thumbs on the tubing opposite the nick two to three cm (one inch) apart and extended toward each other. Push out on the tubing with the thumbs as you pull the sections apart, but do not deliberately bend the glass with the hands. If the tubing does not readily pull apart, the nick probably is too shallow or rounded; make a fresh sharp file scratch in the same place and repeat the operation. Avoid accidental contact of the tubing with a nearby person by standing with your back toward a wall or lab bench. Be careful in cutting a short piece from a long piece of tubing, because the long end may whip and injure another person.

All glass tubing and rods, including stirring rods, should be fire polished before use. Unpolished cut glass has a razorlike edge, which not only can lacerate the skin, but will also cut into a stopper or rubber hose, making it difficult to insert the glass properly. After polishing or bending glass, allow ample time for it to cool before grasping it.

When drilling a stopper, use only a sharp borer one size smaller than that which will just slip over the tube to be inserted. For rubber stoppers, lubricate with water or glycerol. Holes should be bored by slicing through the stopper, twisting with moderate forward pressure, grasping the stopper only with the fingers, and keeping the hand away from the back of the stopper. Keep the index finger of the drilling hand against the barrel of the borer and close to the stopper to stop the borer when it breaks through. Preferably, drill only part way through and then finish by drilling from the opposite side. Discard a stopper if a hole is irregular or does not fit the inserted tube snugly, if it is cracked, or if it leaks. Corks should have been previously softened by rolling and kneading. Rubber or cork stoppers should fit into a joint so that one-third to one-half of the stopper is inserted.

When available, glassware with ground joints is preferable. Glass stoppers and joints should be clean, dry and lightly lubricated.

1.3 Insertion of Glass Tubes or Rods into Stoppers or Flexible Tubing
The following practices will help prevent accidents:
(a) Make sure the diameter of the tube or rod is compatible with the diameter of the hose or stopper.
(b) Fire polish the end of the glass to be inserted; let it cool.
(c) Lubricate the glass. Water may be sufficient; glycerol is a good lubricant.
(d) Wear heavy gloves or wrap layers of cloth around the glass and protect the other hand by holding the hose or stopper with a layered cloth pad.
(e) Hold the glass not more than five cm (two inches) from the end to be inserted.
(f) Insert the glass with a slight twisting motion, avoiding too much pressure and torque.
(g) When helpful, use a cork borer as a sleeve for insertion of glass tubes.
(h) If appropriate, substitute a piece of metal tubing for glass tubing.
(i) Remove stuck tubes by slitting the hose or stopper with a sharp knife.

1.4 Assembling Apparatus
Following these recommendations will help make apparatus assembly easier and equipment use safer:
(a) Keep work space uncluttered.
(b) Set up clean, dry apparatus, firmly clamped and well back from the edge of the lab bench with due regard to the proximity of reagent bottles to burners and to other workers and their equipment. Choose sizes that can properly accommodate the operation to be performed, allowing 20% free space at the minimum.
(c) Use only equipment that is free from flaws such as cracks, chips, frayed wire and obvious defects. Glassware can be examined in polarized light for strains. Even the smallest chip or crack renders glassware unusable; chipped or cracked ware should be repaired or discarded.
(d) A properly placed pan under a reaction vessel or container will confine spilled liquids in the event of glass breakage.
(e) When working with flammable gases or liquids, do not allow burners or other ignition sources in the vicinity. Use appropriate traps, condensers or scrubbers to minimize release of material to the environment. If a hot plate is used, ensure that its temperature

is less than the autoignition temperature of the chemicals likely to be released and that the temperature control device does not spark.

(f) Whenever possible, use controlled electrical heaters or steam in place of gas burners.

(g) Addition and separatory funnels should be properly supported and oriented so that the stopcock will not be loosened by gravity. A retainer ring should be used on the stopcock plug. Glass stopcocks should be freshly lubricated. Teflon stopcocks should not be lubricated.

(h) Condensers should be properly supported with securely positioned clamps and the attached water hoses secured with wire or clamps.

(i) Stirrer motors and vessels should be secured to maintain proper alignment. Magnetic stirring is preferable. Only nonsparking motors should be used in chemical laboratories. Air motors may be an option.

(j) Apparatus attached to a ring stand should be positioned so that the center of gravity of the system is over the base and not to one side. There should be adequate provision for removing burners or baths quickly. Standards bearing heavy loads should be firmly attached to the bench top. Equipment racks should be securely anchored at top and bottom.

(k) Apparatus, equipment or chemical bottles should not be placed on the floor.

(l) A vent should be provided as part of the apparatus for chemicals that are to be heated. Prior to heating a liquid, place boiling stones in unstirred vessels (except test tubes). If a burner is to be used, distribute the heat with a ceramic-centered wire gauze. Use a thermometer in a boiling liquid if there is the possibility of a dangerous exothermic decomposition as in some distillations. This will provide a warning and may allow time to remove the heat and apply external cooling. The setup should allow for fast removal of heat.

(m) Whenever hazardous gases or fumes are likely to be evolved, an appropriate gas trap should be used and the operation confined to a fume hood.

(n) Fume hoods are recommended for all hazardous operations. They are particularly desirable when flammable vapors are evolved as in many distillations. Most vapors have a density greater than that of air and will settle on a bench top or floor where they may diffuse to a distant burner or ignition source. These vapors will roll out over astonishingly long distances, and any ignition can flash back to the source. Once diluted with significant amounts of air, vapors move in air essentially as air itself.

(o) Use a hood when conducting a reaction that could result in an explosion or when using a vacuum system (which may implode). Close the sash to provide a shield. If a hood is not available, use a standing shield. Shields that can be knocked over by an explosion must be stabilized with weights or fasteners. Standing shields are preferably secured near the top. Proper eye and face protection must be worn even when using the shields or hood.

11

2. Equipment Use

2.1 Laboratory Fume Hoods

Fume hoods serve to control exposure to toxic, offensive or flammable vapors. Apparatus used in hoods should be fitted with condensers, traps or scrubbers to contain or collect waste solvents or toxic vapors. The hood is not an appropriate means for disposing of chemicals, nor is it a storage cabinet. Stored chemicals can interfere with efficient hood operation, and in the event of an accident or fire, every item in the hood may become involved.

Before each use, be sure that the hood is working properly. Although not a substitute for a velometer measurement, a continuous monitoring device such as a narrow strip of tissue paper can be used to ensure that the hood is operating. Adequate air flow and the absence of excessive turbulence are necessary for safe operation. Exhaust ports from the hood and supply air vents to the room should not be blocked. Sash openings should be kept to a minimum. Horizontal sashes or combined horizontal and vertical sashes make this easier to do. A hood's air flow can be disrupted by drafts from windows or doors and even by the positions of the workers at the hood. Users should keep their faces outside the plane of the hood sash and should remain alert to changes in air flow. Equipment should be placed as far back in the hood as practical and activities carried out at least 15 cm (six inches) from the front edge of the hood. Finally, to save energy, it may be possible to turn off the blower and close the sashes when the hood is not in use. This should be done only when it is has been determined that the building air balance will not be disturbed.

2.2 Precautions for Using Electrical Equipment

Electrical currents of very low amperage and voltage under certain circumstances may result in fatal shock. Voltages as low as 24 volts ac can be dangerous and present a lethal threat. Low voltage dc circuits do not normally present a hazard to human life, although severe burns are possible. The time of contact with a live circuit affects the degree of damage, especially as far as burns are concerned. Recommendations for minimizing electrical hazards follow:

(a) Only individuals qualified by training or experience should maintain electric or electronic equipment.

(b) Electric wires should never be used as supports. Live wires should not be pulled.

(c) Any electrical failure or any evidence of undue heating of equipment should be reported immediately to the instructor.

(d) All electrical equipment should be periodically inspected to be certain the cords and plugs are in a safe condition and that only three wire grounded, double insulated or isolated wiring is used in 110v-115v ac applications.

2.3 Static Electricity and Spark Hazards

Some protection from static electricity and sparks in hazardous areas and in handling flammable solvents and other chemicals is obtained by proper grounding of containers and equipment and by blanketing with inert gas when needed. Static electricity is magnified by low absolute humidity such as is likely in cold weather. Some common potential sources of sparks and electrostatic discharges are

- ungrounded metal tanks and containers
- clothing or containers made of plastic or synthetic materials
- the making and breaking of an electric circuit while the circuit is energized (switching, pulling plugs)
- temperature control systems in hot plates
- metal-based clamps, nipples, or wire used with nonconducting hoses
- high-pressure gas cylinders upon discharge
- brush motors and hot air dryers

2.4 Centrifuges

If a tabletop centrifuge is used, make certain that it is securely anchored in a location where its vibration will not cause bottles or equipment to fall. The following rules apply to the safe operation of centrifuges:

(a) Always close the centrifuge lid during operation.
(b) Do not leave the centrifuge until full operating speed is attained and the machine appears to be running safely without vibration.
(c) Stop the centrifuge immediately and check the load balances if vibration occurs. Check swing-out buckets for clearance and support.
(d) Regularly clean rotors and buckets with non-corrosive cleaning solutions.

2.5 Ultraviolet Lamps

Two categories of hazards are involved in the use of UV lamps--those inherent in the radiation itself and those associated with operation of the lamps.

All radiation of wavelengths shorter than 250 nm should be considered dangerous. Protective safety glasses with UV-absorbing lenses should be worn when the eyes may be accidentally exposed to light in this wavelength region. It is advisable to operate such UV irradiation systems in a completely closed radiation box. Skin areas exposed to illumination from UV lamps can receive painful burns not unlike severe sunburn, and so precautions should be taken to protect the skin.

Handling of mercury arc lamps will deposit oils from the skin on the outer glass surface. If the residues are not thoroughly removed, they will burn into the glass causing localized buildup of heat during the operation of the lamp. The lamp may then overheat and even crack.

At the end of the useful life of a lamp, buildup of UV-absorbing films on the interior walls of mercury arc lamps may cause the temperature to rise above the safe operating point. Therefore, running-time meters should be attached to such lamps so that the times for discarding the lamps are known. Also, whenever possible, UV sources should be adequately cooled and operated within an enclosure designed to prevent damage by explosion of glass fragments and leakage of mercury vapor.

2.6 Lasers

Because the type and intensity of radiation available from a laser varies widely with instrument design, only generalizations can be made. The following rules apply:

(a) Always wear goggles that offer protection against the specific wavelength of the laser in use. If more than one wavelength is being used, additional goggles specific for each wavelength are required. No available spectacles protect against all laser wavelengths.

(b) Never look directly at the beam or pump source.

(c) Never view the beam pattern directly; use an image converter or other safe, indirect means. To decrease reflecting hazard, do not aim by looking along the beam.

(d) Do not allow any objects that cause reflections to be present in or along the beam. Even buttons on clothing and polished screw heads can be dangerous.

(e) Keep a high general illumination level in areas where lasers are in operation. Low light levels cause dilation of the pupils, thereby increasing the hazard.

(f) Display warning signs in laser areas.

2.7 X-ray Generators and Particle Accelerators

These instruments can be dangerous because of the radiation generated and the high voltages available from their power supplies. All regulations of the Nuclear Regulatory Commission, state department of public health and radiological health service must be followed. Warning signs must be displayed on or near the main power switch of the instrument.

2.8 Hazards from Radioactive Materials

All work requiring the use of radioactive materials must be performed under the direction of the person responsible for the laboratory and coordinated through the institution's radiation safety officer. Radioactive materials, the vessels in which they are used, and the work area must be clearly labeled as a potential radiation danger.

Anyone considering the use of radioactive materials should consult the person in charge for advice on the regulations concerning procurement, handling and disposal. All waste radioactive materials or materials suspected of being radioactive must be disposed of by the person responsible in accord with state and federal regulations. All individuals planning to work with radioactive materials are strongly encouraged to complete a course on the safe handling of such materials before they begin using them.

2.9 Compressed Gases

Gases used in laboratories are often conveniently supplied in cylinders at high pressure. Their use compounds potential chemical hazards. The rules for the proper use of compressed gases include:

(a) Handle cylinders of compressed gases as high-energy sources and therefore as potential explosives.

(b) Restrain cylinders of all sizes, empty or full, individually by straps, chains, or a suitable stand to prevent them from falling.

(c) When storing or moving cylinders, have the protective caps securely in place to protect the valve stems.

(d) When moving large cylinders, strap them to properly designed, wheeled carts to ensure stability.

(e) Do not expose cylinders to temperatures higher than about 50° C. Some rupture devices on cylinders will release at about 65° C. Some small cylinders, such as lecture bottles, are not fitted with rupture devices and may explode if exposed to high temperatures.

(f) Never use cylinders that cannot be identified positively.

(g) Never lubricate, modify, force, or tamper with cylinder valves.

(h) Use toxic, flammable, or reactive gases in fume hoods only. Cylinders should be stored in appropriately ventilated cabinets or in an open storage area.

(i) Never direct high-pressure gases at a person.

(j) Do not use compressed gas or compressed air to blow away dust or dirt; the resultant flying particles are dangerous.

(k) Be aware that rapid release of a compressed gas will cause an unsecured gas hose to whip dangerously and also may build up a static charge that could ignite a combustible gas.

(l) Do not extinguish a flame involving a highly combustible gas until the source of gas has been shut off; otherwise, it can reignite causing an explosion.

(m) Close the main cylinder valves tightly when not in use.

(n) Promptly remove the regulators from empty cylinders and replace the protective caps at once. Mark the empty cylinder.

(o) Never bleed cylinders completely empty. Leave a slight pressure to keep contaminants out.

(p) Use the appropriate regulator on each gas cylinder. The threads on the regulators are designed to avoid improper use. Adaptors or homemade modifications can be dangerous.

(q) Do not put oil or grease on the high pressure side of an oxygen, chlorine, or other oxidizing agent cylinder. A fire or explosion can result.

(r) Always wear safety glasses when handling and using compressed gases.

(s) Observe the following special rules when working with acetylene cylinders.

- Always store acetylene cylinders upright. They are partially filled with acetone.
- Do not use a cylinder which has been stored or handled in a nonupright position until it has remained in an upright position for at least 30 minutes.
- Ensure that the outlet line of an acetylene cylinder is protected with a flash arrester.
- Never exceed the pressure limit indicated by the warning red line of an acetylene pressure gauge.
- Use the correct kind of tubing to transport the gaseous acetylene. Some tubing materials such as copper form explosive acetylides.

3. Separations
3.1 Extractions

Extractions can present a hazard because of the potential buildup of pressure from a volatile solvent and an immiscible aqueous phase. Glass separatory funnels used in laboratory operations are particularly susceptible to problems because their stoppers or stopcocks can be forced out, resulting in a spill of the contained liquid. It is even possible for pressure to burst the vessel. Here is the way to use a separatory funnel correctly.

Do not attempt to extract a solution until it is cooler than the boiling point of the extractant. When a volatile solvent is used, the unstoppered separatory funnel should first be swirled to allow some solvent to vaporize and expel some air. Close the funnel and invert it with the stopper held in place and immediately open the stopcock to release more air plus vapor. This should be done with the hand encompassing the barrel to keep the stopcock plug securely seated. (Glass stopcocks should be lubricated.) Do not vent the separatory funnel near a flame or other ignition source. Then close the stopcock, shake with a swirl, and immediately open the stopcock with the funnel in the inverted position to again vent the vapors. If it is necessary to use a separatory funnel larger than 1 liter for an extraction with a volatile solvent, the force on the stopper may be too great and cause the stopper to be expelled. Consider performing the extraction in several smaller batches.

3.2 Distillations

Distillation is probably the most common method of separation and purification used in laboratory and industrial operations. Potential dangers arise from pressure buildup, the common use of flammable materials, and the necessity for heat to vaporize the chemicals involved. A variety of apparatus designs are used to accomplish distillations at atmospheric pressure, under inert atmospheres, at reduced pressure (vacuum distillation), and by the addition of steam to the distillation mixture (steam distillation).

Careful design and construction of the distillation system is required to accomplish effective separation and to avoid leaks that can lead to fires or contamination of the work area. It is necessary to ensure smooth boiling during the separation process and to avoid bumping which can blow apart the distillation apparatus. Stirring the distillation mixture is the best method to avoid bumping.

The use of boiling stones is only effective for distillations carried out at atmospheric pressure. Be sure that fresh boiling stones are used when a liquid is to be boiled without stirring. Do not add boiling stones or any other solid material to a liquid that is near its boiling point because this may cause it to boil over spontaneously.

The source of heat is an important factor in the distillation process. Even heating can best be done by using an electric mantle heater, a ceramic cavity heater, steam coils, or a nonflammable liquid bath. Silicone oil or another suitable high-boiling oil can be used if heated on a hot plate. Hot water or steam may be used where practical. An additional thermometer may be inserted very near the center bottom of the distilling flask to warn of dangerous, exothermic decomposition. Always avoid heating above the temperature directed in the procedure.

Organic compounds must never be distilled or evaporated to dryness unless they are known to be free of peroxides. Most ethers, including cyclic ethers, form dangerously explosive peroxides on exposure to air and light. Many alcohols, unsaturated hydrocarbons, potassium metal, and other reagents can also form peroxides.

Superheating and sudden boiling (bumping) frequently occur when distilling using reduced pressure. Therefore, it is important that the assembly be secure and the heat be distributed more evenly than is possible with a flame. Evacuate the assembly gradually to minimize the possibility of bumping. Stirring or an air or nitrogen bleed tube provides good vaporization without overheating and decomposition. A standing shield should be in place for protection in the event of an implosion. After finishing a reduced pressure distillation, cool the system before slowly bleeding in air because air may induce an explosion in a hot system. Pure nitrogen is always preferred to air and can be used even before cooling the system. Refer to paragraph 4.3 for the safe use of cold traps during reduced pressure distillation.

When carrying out a steam distillation, minimize the accumulation of condensate in the distillation flask. Remember that the heat of condensation of steam is very high. Overfilling the flask is less likely if condensation from the entering steam line is trapped, and if the flask is heated or insulated to prevent excessive condensation. Do not flood the condenser by running the steam in too fast.

4. Temperature Control

Many reactions must be initiated by heating. Since the rates of most reactions increase as the temperature increases, highly exothermic reactions can become dangerously violent unless provisions are made for adequate cooling. If too much of a reagent has been added initially, late induction of the reaction can cause it to become too vigorous for effective condensation of vapors unless a cooling bath is quickly applied to the reaction vessel. Viscous liquids transfer heat poorly and require special precautions. Reactions usually require some temperature control, and the apparatus should be assembled in such a way that either heating or cooling can be applied or withdrawn readily.

Test tubes should be held with a test tube holder and heated gently along the side, not at the bottom, to minimize superheating, which may cause the contents to be ejected. Avoid pointing a test tube toward yourself or any nearby person. If possible, test tubes should be heated by placing them in a suitable hot water or hot oil bath.

4.1 Oil and Sand Baths

When hot oil or sand is used for heating purposes, extreme care must be taken to avoid overturning the bath, hazardous splattering caused by water falling into hot oil or hot sand, smoking caused by decomposition of the oil or of organic materials in the oil, and fire caused by overheated oil bursting into flames. Ensure proper labeling which includes the name of the oil and its safe working temperatures. Operating baths should not be left unattended without a warning label (hot oil) and a high-temperature shutoff. Precautions should be taken to contain any spills of hot oil caused by breakage or overturning of the baths.

Important considerations when these types of baths are used include the

- size and location of the bath
- operating temperature and temperature control devices
- type of oil used; e.g., silicone oil, Dow Corning 550, is suggested for most heating needs
- available ventilation
- method of cooling the hot oil
- storage of oil for reuse
- location away from possible sources of spilled water or chemicals

4.2 Cooling Baths and Cold Traps

When ice water is not cool enough for use as a bath, salt and ice may be used. For even lower temperatures, dry ice may be used with an organic liquid. An ideal cooling liquid for use with dry ice should have the following characteristics:

(1) nontoxic vapors
(2) low viscosity
(3) nonflammability
(4) low volatility

Ether, acetone and butanone are too volatile and flammable. The final choice of a liquid will also depend on the temperature requirements. Although no substance meets all these criteria, the following are suggested (numbers in parentheses signify above criteria which are not met):

- ethylene glycol or propylene glycol in a 3:2 ratio with water and thinned with isopropyl alcohol (criterion 2)
- isopropyl alcohol (criterion 3)
- some glycol ethers (criterion 2)

Add the dry ice to the liquid, or the liquid to the dry ice, in small increments. Wait for the foaming to stop before proceeding with the addition. The rate of addition can be increased gradually as the liquid cools.

Cryogenic coolants should always be used with caution; cryogenic liquids must be handled in properly vented containers. Be aware that very low temperature coolants may condense oxygen and cause an explosion with combustible materials. Use gloves and face shields and immerse the object to be cooled slowly to avoid too vigorous boiling and overflow of the coolant. Glass Dewar flasks should be of borosilicate glass and protected by covering with cloth-backed friction or duct tape or a metal casing to contain flying pieces in the event of implosion. Avoid pouring cold liquid onto the edge of a glass Dewar flask when filling because the flask may break and implode. For the same reason do not pour liquid nitrogen out of a glass Dewar flask; use mild air pressure or a siphon. Metal or plastic Dewar type flasks are preferable and eliminate this problem. Never use a household Thermos bottle in place of a Dewar flask.

Do not lower your head into a dry ice chest. Because no oxygen is present, suffocation can result. Do not handle the dry ice with bare hands; if the skin is even slightly moist, severe burns can result. Use dry leather or suitable cryo-gloves. When chipping dry ice, wear goggles.

4.3 Reduced Pressure Operations

Vacuum desiccators should be protected by covering with cloth-backed friction or duct tape or enclosed in a box or approved shielding device for protection in case of an implosion. Only chemicals being dehydrated should be stored in a desiccator. Before opening a desiccator that is under reduced pressure, make sure that atmospheric pressure has been restored. A "frozen" desiccator lid can be loosened by using a single-edge razor blade as a wedge that is then tapped with a wooden block to raise the lid.

All vacuum lines should be trapped and shielding should be used whenever the apparatus is under reduced pressure.

Water aspirators for reduced pressure are used mainly for filtration purposes, and only equipment that is approved for this purpose should be used. Never apply reduced pressure to a flat-bottomed flask unless it is a heavy-walled filter flask designed for the purpose. Place a trap and a check valve between the aspirator and the apparatus so that water cannot be sucked back into the system if the water pressure should fall unexpectedly while filtering. These recommendations also apply to rotary evaporation equipment where water aspirators are being used for reduced pressure.

If vacuum pumps are used, a cold trap should be placed between the apparatus and the vacuum pump so that volatiles from a reaction or distillation do not get into the pump oil or out into the atmosphere of the laboratory. When possible, exhausts from pumps should be vented to a hood. Pumps with belt drives should also have belt guards to prevent hands or loose clothing from being caught in the belt pulley.

Section III
Guide to Chemical Hazards

1. Toxicity

"What is it that is not poison? All things are poison and nothing is without poison. It is the dose only that makes a thing not a poison", Paracelsus wrote these sentences in the fifteenth century. It has long been known that anything when ingested in sufficient quantity can be lethal. Toxicity is frequently subdivided into acute and chronic effects. Acute poisons produce an immediate effect, usually from a single dose. Hydrogen sulfide in high concentrations would be considered an acute poison. Chronic effects result from low doses accumulated over long periods of time. Carcinogens and some neurotoxins are generally considered chronic poisons.

A detailed discussion of toxicity is beyond the scope of this booklet. All individuals who handle chemicals should supplement the information below with specific details applicable to their laboratories by consulting Appendix II for a list of additional reference material.

Any substance can be harmful to living things. But, just as there are degrees of being harmful, so are there also degrees of being safe. A complex relationship exists between a material and its biological effect in humans that involves considerations of dose (the amount of a substance to which one is exposed), the length of time of the exposure, the route of exposure (inhalation, ingestion, absorption through the skin or eyes), and myriad other factors such as sex, stage in the reproductive cycle, age, lifestyle, previous sensitization, allergic factors, and even genetic disposition.

There are four main routes by which hazardous chemicals enter the body:

- Absorption through the respiratory tract (lungs) through inhalation. This is the most important route in terms of severity.
- Absorption through the digestive tract. This can occur through eating or smoking with contaminated hands or in contaminated work areas.
- Absorption through the skin. This is the most common cause of occupational disease (dermatitis).
- Percutaneous injection through the skin. This can occur through misuse of sharp materials especially hypodermic needles. Toxic effects can be immediate or delayed; reversible or irreversible; local or systemic.

The toxic effects of chemicals can vary from mild and reversible, (*e.g.,* a headache from a single episode of inhaling the vapors of petroleum naphtha that disappears when the victim gets fresh air) to serious and irreversible (*e.g.,* birth defects from excessive exposures during pregnancy or cancer from exposures to carcinogens).

There are several types of toxic effects.

- *Acute poisoning* is characterized by rapid absorption of the substance and the exposure is sudden and severe. Normally, a single large exposure is involved. Examples: carbon monoxide or cyanide poisoning.
- *Chronic poisoning* is characterized by prolonged or repeated

exposure of a duration measured in days, months or years. Symptoms may not be immediately apparent. Examples: lead or mercury poisoning and pesticide exposure.

- *Cumulative poisons* are characterized by materials that tend to build up in the body as a result of numerous chronic exposures. The effects are not seen until a critical body burden is reached. Example: heavy metals.
- *Substances in Combination:* When two or more hazardous materials are present at the same time, the resulting effect can be greater than the effect predicted based on the individual substances. This is called a synergistic or potentiating effect. Example: exposure to alcohol and chlorinated solvents.

The toxic effects from exposure to a chemical depend upon the severity of the exposures. Generally, the more, or the more often the exposure, the more severe the result.

Most exposure standards are based on time weighted averages. The time weighted average (TWA) is based on the average exposure weighted for an 8 hour work day. Ceiling (C) limits and acceptable maximum peaks above the average must be considered when exposures are evaluated. High peak exposures may have health implications even when the average exposure is not very high.

Exposure limits are expressed as the Threshold Limit Value (TLV) or the Permissible Exposure Limit (PEL). The TLV is a recommended occupational exposure standard which is published by the American Conference of Governmental Industrial Hygienists (ACGIH). TLVs are expressed as part of vapor or gas per million parts of air by volume (ppm) or as approximate milligrams of particulate per cubic meter of air (mg/m^3). The TLV is the average concentration of a chemical that is thought most people can be exposed to for a working lifetime with no ill effects. The TLV is an advisory guideline. If applicable, a ceiling concentration (C) which should not be exceeded or a skin hazard (S) will be indicated with the TLV. The permissible exposure limit (PEL) is a legal standard issued by OSHA. The PEL for a given chemical is often almost identical to the TLV.

TLVs have been established for approximately 850 chemicals. In January, 1989, OSHA issued a final rule setting new or revised PELs for 600 substances. In its rule making, OSHA used the *1987-88 Threshold Limit Values (TLVs)* published by the American Conference of Governmental Industrial Hygienists and the Recommended Exposure Limits (RELs) developed by the National Institute of Occupational Safety and Health. In this rule making, OSHA also regulated skin exposure to many chemicals.

Material safety data sheets (MSDSs) for hazardous chemicals and mixtures of hazardous chemicals cite the TLVs or PELs for the subject chemicals or mixtures. The safety officer should ensure by appropriate measurements of the breathing air that all persons who work with hazardous chemicals are exposed at concentrations less than the TLV or PEL. Several methods are available to make the appropriate measurements and to suggest ways to improve the ventilation. Since TLVs have not been established for all compounds, they may not be listed on the MSDS. If available, the results of animal testing may provide some guidance. In rare cases, the chemical is not harmful to inhale and no limit is necessary.

A variety of allergens (agents that can produce an immunologic reaction) may be encountered in the laboratory when suitable precautions are not enforced. Further, some chemicals evoke nonimmunologic reactions in individuals who are sensitive to them. Typical responses include dermatitis or asthma. The special problem is one of sensitization. Difficulties can also arise because the allergic response may not be readily identifiable. There is usually no physical reaction at the time of initial exposure although this is the point at which sensitization may have occurred. The physical reaction then takes place after the next, or some subsequent exposure. Unfortunately, no common listing is available for compounds observed to act as allergens. Refer to NIOSH Allergenic lists and the appropriate material safety data sheets.

There are many factors influencing the toxicity of chemicals; some known, some not yet fully understood. Hence all chemicals should be handled with respect for their known or potential hazards. Skin, eyes and respiratory tract should always be protected from possible exposure by use of engineering controls including fume hoods and room ventilation, appropriate protective equipment, and safe work practices including personal hygiene practices. Eating, drinking, smoking and the application of cosmetics should be strictly prohibited in all areas where chemicals are handled or stored. Thorough washing with soap and water should be mandatory at the end of a laboratory period and before leaving the area during a break. These precautions can prevent many undesirable toxic consequences.

2. Sources of Information
2.1 Labels

Most chemists consider and evaluate chemical hazards in four categories--toxic, flammable, corrosive and reactive. Container labels generally convey this hazard information. It should be stressed that all chemical containers must have labels. *Before using any chemical, it is important to read and heed the label.* However, remember that in the case of multiple hazards, the label may only indicate the most immediate one.

2.2 Material Safety Data Sheets (MSDSs)

A material safety data sheet must be available for every chemical used. The MSDS represents a starting point reflecting information known at the time of preparation and the instructor may add supplementary information to any area.

The following section gives detailed instructions for reading material safety data sheets. There is a specific list of items that are required to be on a MSDS. Each such item, with an explanation of its meaning, follows:

(a) Chemical name—usually the IUPAC (International Union of Pure Applied Chemistry) or Chemical Abstracts Service chemical name is given, but it also may be a common name for the chemical (*e. g.* ethylene glycol is acceptable instead of 1,2-ethanediol). Trade names may be supplied but the chemical name is also required unless it is considered to be a trade secret.

(b) CAS Registry Number—This number is not required by OSHA but most state Right-to-Know laws require it. This number is assigned to each chemical by Chemical Abstracts Service. There are a few instances where a chemical has several different numbers, a few chemicals have no assigned number and most mixtures do not have assigned numbers.

(c) Date Prepared—OSHA requires that the date of preparation or latest update be on the MSDS.

(d) Composition of Mixtures—This includes all hazardous materials over 1%, and all carcinogens over 0.1%. Trade names can be used but chemical names must also be included unless this information is considered a trade secret.

(e) OSHA PEL—This is either a time-weighted average limit for an 8 hour day or a maximum concentration exposure limit for those items on the OSHA list. The figures may be in parts per million (ppm) or mg per cubic meter (mg/m^3).

(f) ACGIH TLV—Maximum exposure limits recommended by the American Conference of Governmental Industrial Hygienists. The same measuring units specified in the OSHA PEL are applicable. The ACGIH TLV list is updated each year.

(g) Health Effects—Identification of target organs or systems adversely affected by overexposure.

(h) Physical/Chemical Characteristics—This usually includes the following items where applicable:
- Boiling point—the value may be at reduced pressure and either in degrees Celsius or Fahrenheit
- Melting point
- Vapor pressure—usually in mm Hg; the temperature must be specified (usually in the range of normal room temperature)
- Specific gravity (density with respect to water at a specified temperature)
- Solubility in water—approximate values are acceptable
- Appearance and odor
- Evaporation rate—usually relative to butyl acetate

(i) Fire and Explosion Hazard Data—This usually includes the following items:
- Flash point—There are several methods of establishing the flash point; the method should be specified. In general, the flash point of the chemical is the temperature at which its vapor can be ignited.
- Auto ignition temperature—the temperature at which a chemical ignites spontaneously in the air.
- Flammability limits—Most volatile chemicals have lower and upper concentrations in air below and above which they cannot be ignited.
- Recommended extinguishing media
- Unusual fire and explosion hazards

(j) Reactivity Hazard Data—Information should include whether the material is unstable and under what conditions instability exists, incompatibilities, and whether hazardous decomposition products can be produced.

(k) Health Hazard Data—This topic includes one or more of the following:
- LD50 (lethal dose 50)—This is the lethal single dose (usually oral) in mg/kg (milligrams of chemical per kilogram of animal

body weight) of a chemical that is expected to kill 50% of a test animal population.

- LC50 (lethal concentration 50)—This is a concentration dose expressed as ppm for gases and vapors or as micrograms of material per liter of air for dusts and mists expected to kill 50% of a test animal population in one exposure.

In the Health Hazard Data Section, MSDSs often use words or phrases such as avoid contact, flammable, and others. Generalized descriptions of many of these phrases and the precautions to be practiced follow: .

- AVOID CONTACT: General rule for *all* chemicals, even if they are considered non-hazardous.
  PRECAUTIONS: Do not breathe vapors and avoid contact with skin, eyes and clothing for all chemicals handled.
- CARCINOGEN: Substances which are suspected or known to cause cancer. Some may have threshold limits of exposure.
  PRECAUTIONS: Exercise extreme care when handling! Do not breathe vapors and avoid all contact with skin, eyes and clothing by wearing suitable protective equipment and using appropriate confining apparatus.
- CORROSIVE: Living tissue as well as equipment is destroyed on contact with these chemicals.
  PRECAUTIONS: Do not breathe vapors and avoid contact with skin, eyes and clothing. Use suitable protective equipment.
- DANGER: Substances that have known harmful effects or which may have harmful effects, but have no available literature citing such effects.
  PRECAUTIONS: Treat as if these are the most dangerous chemicals that exist. There may or may not be serious hazards associated with these chemicals.
- EXPLOSIVE: Substances known to explode under some conditions.
  PRECAUTIONS: Avoid shock (dropping), friction, sparks and heat. Isolate from other chemicals which become hazardous when spilled.
- FLAMMABLE: Substances which give off vapors that readily ignite under usual working conditions
  PRECAUTIONS: Spontaneously flammable --Avoid contact with air /Flammable liquids, gases, vapors --Keep away from heat, sparks, or open flame Sensitive to moisture --Keep dry
- IRRITANT: Substances that have an irritant effect on skin, eyes, respiratory tract, etc.
  PRECAUTIONS: Do not breathe vapors and avoid contact with skin and eyes.
- LACHRYMATOR: Substances that have an irritant or burning effect on skin, eye or respiratory tract. These

	are dangerous in very small quantities (opening the cap has an immediate effect on eyes).
PRECAUTIONS:	Only open in a hood! Do not breathe vapors. Avoid contact with skin, eyes. Avoid heating.

- MUTAGEN: Chemical or physical agents that cause genetic alterations.

  PRECAUTIONS: Handle with extreme care! Do not breathe vapors and avoid contact with skin, eyes and clothing.

- PEROXIDE FORMER: Substances which form peroxides or hydroperoxides upon standing or when in contact with air.

  PRECAUTIONS: Many peroxides are explosive! Do not open bottle if a residue is present on the outside of the cap or inside of the bottle!

- POISON: Substances that have very serious and often irreversible effects on the body. Hazardous when breathed, swallowed, or in contact with the skin, and in sufficient quantity lead to death. The Department of Transportation regulations classify many poisons for transportation.

  PRECAUTIONS: Avoid all contact with the body. When handling use suitable protective equipment.

- STENCH: Substances which have or generate bad smelling odors.

  PRECAUTIONS: Open only in a hood.

- TERATOGEN: Substances that cause the production of physical defects in a developing fetus or embryo.

  PRECAUTIONS: Handle with extreme care! Do not breathe vapors and avoid contact with skin, eyes and clothing. Use suitable protective equipment when handling.

- TOXIC: Substances which are hazardous to health when breathed, swallowed, or are in contact with the skin. There is danger of serious damage to health by short or prolonged exposure.

  PRECAUTIONS: Avoid all contact with the body. When handling use suitable protective equipment.

(l) First Aid—Appropriate procedures for emergency first aid should be given in the MSDS.

(m) Precautions for Spills and Cleanup--Appropriate steps for safe cleanup of a spill or release should be given. An appropriate waste disposal method including whether the material can be put in a landfill or other EPA approved disposal facility should be supplied in the MSDS.

(n) Control Measures—Types of protective clothing, gloves and respiratory protection should be listed. If the material should always be handled in a hood, glovebox or with extra ventilation, it should be listed under this heading.

Material safety data sheets provide unique opportunities for students to learn how decisions are made in using chemicals. The section describing chemical reactivity will include information on the incompatibility of chemicals, and students should understand the basis for the recommendations regarding the compatibility of chemical compounds as well as the practical implications. For example, acetic acid should not be mixed with chromic oxide, nitric acid, perchloric acid or potassium permanganate. Therefore one should not store acetic acid next to perchloric acid or mix a waste containing acetic acid with a waste containing nitric acid. Logically, if it were necessary to bring together acetic acid and any one or more of its "incompatible" compounds, it would be important to limit the amounts used and to carefully control experimental conditions. The practical information found in the reactivity section of a MSDS is very important in designing safe experimental procedures.

3. Predicting Chemical Hazards

There are millions of chemicals, but relatively few have been described in detail. Chemists know that compounds can be classified based on chemical properties, and that certain classes of compounds can react with each other to produce various combinations of toxic products, heat, fire and explosions. Examples of classes that must be considered in safety planning include the following:

- oxidizing agents and reducing agents
- corrosives such as acids and bases
- water reactive chemicals
- air reactive chemicals
- highly toxic chemicals

For example, acetic acid is an acid but it is also a reducing agent. Chromic acid, nitric acid, perchloric acid and potassium permanganate are oxidizing agents. These two classes (reducing and oxidizing agents) are likely to react with each other. Thus, if one can place compounds into classes and know that certain mixtures of classes of compounds are incompatible, one can begin to predict hazardous situations.

Appendix III of this manual lists examples of incompatible compounds as well as classes of compounds which can be harmful when they react with each other. This list can be used to classify compounds and predict incompatibility. Bretherick's book, *Handbook of Reactive Chemical Hazards,* and NFPA (National Fire Protection Association) 491M, *Manual of Hazardous Chemical Reactions,* provide additional information. The ability to classify chemicals which are not on the lists and to predict accurately their reaction characteristics is improved by experience.

3.1 Solvents

Solvents are the most frequently encountered compounds which present flammability hazards, *i.e.*, will ignite easily and burn rapidly. Note that a flammable liquid itself does not burn; it is the vapor from the liquid that burns. The rate at which a liquid produces flammable vapors depends to some extent on its vapor pressure. The vaporization rate increases as the temperature increases. Therefore, a flammable liquid is more hazardous at elevated temperatures than at normal temperatures. Most organic solvents such as acetone and pentane must be kept away from inadvertent contact with ignition sources or oxidizers. For more information on solvent flammability and storage, refer to Appendix IV.

Benzene and many halogenated hydrocarbons are suspected human carcinogens. Chronic poisoning can occur by inhalation of relatively small amounts of benzene over a long period of time. Exposure to the liquids and their vapors should be avoided. Halogenated hydrocarbons like some other solvents can also be absorbed through the skin. Contact of solvents with the skin should be avoided because of potential skin absorption and because contact causes dryness and cracking of the skin, which opens the way to infection and allergic responses. The material safety data sheets should be consulted before proceeding with an experiment involving any of these substances.

Many common solvents, especially ethers, can form potentially explosive peroxides. These solvents are particularly dangerous when they are evaporated to dryness. For information on peroxide handing and disposal, see paragraph 3.4 of this section and the Overview for Faculty and Administrators.

3.2 Acids and Bases

Acids and bases represent the class of compounds most often encountered which present corrosivity hazards, *i.e.*, cause visible destruction of, or irreversible alterations at, the site of contact. These corrosive chemicals attack the skin and can cause permanent damage to the eyes.

All of the hydrogen halides are acids and all are serious respiratory irritants. Hydrogen fluoride poses a special danger. Both its gas and solutions are toxic and it is rapidly absorbed through the skin, penetrating deeply into the body tissues. Contact with dilute solutions of hydrogen fluoride may be painless for several hours, but serious burns result. In all cases, immediate and thorough flushing with water and immediate attention by a physician who is prepared to treat hydrogen fluoride burns is necessary.

Oxyacids such as sulfuric and nitric acid have widely differing properties. Sulfuric acid is a very strong dehydrating agent and is available as the pure material or as fuming sulfuric acid (oleum). When preparing solutions, always add the acid to water and remember that the large heat of solution may produce a large increase in temperature. Nitric acid is a strong oxidizing agent which acts rapidly and turns exposed skin brown as a denaturing reaction occurs.

Perchloric acid is a powerful oxidizing agent that may react explosively with organic compounds and other reducing agents. It must be used only in a water wash-down fume hood of noncombustible construction. Frequent inspections should be made to prevent perchloric acid and perchlorate accumulation in the exhaust system of the fume hood. Do not use near wooden tables or benches. Keep perchloric acid bottles on glass or ceramic trays that are large enough to hold all the acid if the bottle breaks. Organic matter should be digested with nitric acid before addition of perchloric acid. Never heat perchloric acid with sulfuric acid because dehydration may produce anhydrous perchloric acid which is explosive. Perchlorate esters have the same shattering effect as nitroglycerine. Transition metal perchlorates are capable of exploding.

Dry picric acid is a high explosive and should be purchased only when specifically required and with a thorough understanding of its hazards. Although not explosive when wet, picric acid solutions may evaporate to leave the hazardous solid. Old containers of picric acid such as occasionally found in stockrooms should be disposed of only with expert assistance.

The most common bases found in academic laboratories include the alkali metal hydroxides and aqueous solutions of ammonia. Sodium and potassium hydroxides are extremely destructive to both the skin and tissues of the eye. Caution is required when preparing concentrated solutions of these bases because the large heat of solution can raise the temperature to dangerous levels. The vapors of ammonia solutions are such strong irritants that these solutions should be used in the hood.

3.3 Other Toxic Materials

The halogens are all toxic. Chlorine is a gas that must be handled with proper traps and ventilation. Bromine, a liquid, is a lachrymator that can cause serious burns on skin contact.

Mercury is a cumulative poison. The fact that metallic mercury is widely used from grade school through graduate school justifies a special alert to its dangers. Pouring without splashing or spilling is difficult. Spilled mercury will roll when it hits a hard surface, possibly breaking into droplets too tiny to be seen. Even visible droplets can adhere to smooth vertical surfaces, and so the cleanup must be thorough.

Spilled mercury should be immediately and thoroughly cleaned up using an aspirator bulb or a special vacuum device. If a mercury cleanup unit is available, become familiar with its location and proper use. Mercury spilled into floor cracks can be made nonvolatile by amalgamation with zinc dust. Household vacuum cleaners must not be used because they will redisperse mercury aerosols and spread the contamination.

Formaldehyde is a colorless, pungent, irritant gas that is water soluble and is most frequently marketed as 37-56% aqueous solutions, commonly known as formalin. It is also sold as a solid polymer (paraformaldehyde) that decomposes to its monomer upon heating. Inhalation of the vapors may result in severe irritation of the upper respiratory tract and edema. Formaldehyde is a severe eye irritant, causing delayed effects that are not appreciably eased by eye washing. Skin sensitization can result from repeated exposure. Because repeated exposure to formaldehyde can lead to a formaldehyde allergy, avoid skin contact with aqueous solutions by appropriate use of neoprene, butyl rubber, or polyvinyl chloride gloves. Formaldehyde is an anticipated human carcinogen.

Cyanides and nitriles are among the most toxic and rapidly acting substances encountered in the chemical laboratory. Symptoms of toxicity occur if these materials are swallowed, inhaled, or absorbed through the skin. A few inhalations of hydrogen cyanide can be fatal. Metal cyanides are converted to hydrogen cyanide in the presence of acid. Laboratories using cyanides should have antidotes (nitrite and thiosulfates) readily available.

3.4 Organic Peroxides and Peroxide Formers

Organic peroxides are a special class of compounds which pose unusual stability problems. These peroxides are among the most hazardous chemicals normally handled in chemical laboratories and in manufacturing. As a class, organic peroxides are low-power explosives. They are hazardous because of their extreme sensitivity to shock, sparks or other forms of accidental ignition. Many peroxides that are routinely handled in laboratories are more sensitive to shock than primary explosives such as TNT. Peroxides have a specific half-life, or rate of decomposition, under any given set of conditions. A low rate of decomposition may autoaccelerate into a violent explosion, especially in bulk quantities of peroxides. They are sensitive to heat, friction, impact, and light as well as to strong oxidizing and reducing agents. All organic peroxides are extremely flammable, and fires involving bulk quantities of peroxides should be approached with extreme caution. A peroxide present as a contaminating reagent in a solvent can change the course of a planned reaction.

Compounds of the following types are known to form peroxides:

- Aldehydes.
- Ethers, especially cyclic ethers, and ethers derived from primary and secondary alcohols. It is especially important to label the containers of ethyl or isopropyl ether with the date they are opened, so that the contents of the container can be destroyed by the user within three months. Ethers must never be distilled unless known to be free of peroxides.
- Compounds containing benzylic hydrogen atoms. Such compounds are especially susceptible to peroxide formation if the hydrogens are on tertiary carbon atoms, *e.g.*, cumene (isopropyl benzene).
- Compounds containing the allylic ($CH_2=CHCH_2-$) structure, including most alkenes.
- Ketones, especially cyclic ketones.
- Vinyl and vinylidene compounds, *e.g.*, vinyl acetate and vinylidene chloride.

Specific examples of chemicals that can form dangerous concentrations of peroxides with exposure to air are

- cyclohexene
- cyclooctene
- decalin (decahydronaphthalene)
- p-dioxane
- ethyl ether
- isopropyl ether
- tetrahydrofuran (THF)
- tetralin (tetrahydronaphthalene)

Several acceptable colorimetric tests for peroxides in ethers are available. If there is sufficient peroxide present to form a precipitate, the container and its contents must be discarded with extreme care. If a test is positive, filter the contaminated liquid through a column of chromatographic, basic-grade, aluminum oxide until the test is negative. Promptly discard the contaminated alumina in the appropriate solid waste container. It has been suggested that if you think you ought to make a test for the presence of peroxides, then you have probably kept the material too long and should dispose of it immediately in a suitable manner. A test for peroxides should only be attempted if it is clear that no danger will result from moving or opening the container. Solids observed in the liquid or around the cap can indicate dangerous peroxide buildup. Store peroxide formers away from heat and light in closed vessels, preferably in the container furnished by the supplier.

The following precautions should be followed when handling organic peroxides and hydroperoxides:

(a) Study and follow all precautions specified by the manufacturer of the peroxy substance before using it.

(b) Store the peroxides at the minimum safe temperatures to minimize the rate of decomposition. CAUTION: Do not refrigerate liquid or solutions of peroxides at or below the temperature at which the peroxide freezes or precipitates. Peroxides in these forms are extra sensitive to shock and heat.

(c) Limit the quantity of peroxide handled to the minimum amount required. Don't return unused peroxide to the stock container.

(d) Clean up all spills immediately by recommended procedures. The first step is usually to dilute or disperse the peroxide with an inert substance.

(e) The sensitivity of most peroxides to shock and heat can be reduced by dilution with inert solvents such as aliphatic hydrocarbons (*e.g.*, mineral oil) but NEVER with acetone or other ketones.

(f) Avoid using solutions of peroxides in volatile solvents when it is possible that the solvent will vaporize and thereby increase the peroxide concentration.

(g) Never use a metal spatula with organic peroxides. Contamination by metals can cause explosive decomposition. Use ceramic or plastic spatulas instead.

(h) Do not permit smoking, open flames, sparking equipment or any source of intense heat near peroxides.

(i) Avoid friction, grinding, and all forms of impact, especially with solid organic peroxides. NEVER use glass containers with screw cap lids or glass stoppers. Instead, use plastic (*e.g.*, polyethylene) bottles and sealers.

(j) Because peroxy compounds are generally irritants, avoid ingestion, inhalation, and skin contact. Treat any areas of contact as burns and get medical attention.

For recommendations on disposing of peroxides, see the section for faculty and administrators.

Section IV
Safety Equipment and Emergency Procedures

Chemistry laboratories have a variety of equipment to be used in case an accident occurs. Each person in a laboratory must be familiar with the locations of, and procedures for using, this equipment. The safety equipment will usually include an eyewash fountain, safety shower, fire extinguisher, and an alarm or telephone system. The laboratory will have a plan for everyone to follow if an evacuation is ever necessary. Be sure that you know the main and alternate evacuation routes as well as the procedures for accounting for each person in the laboratory.

1. General Information

As much as possible, follow procedures that have been established and practiced. When helping another person, remember to evaluate the potential danger to yourself before taking action. When an emergency occurs, the following actions are recommended:

(a) Report the nature and location of the emergency to the instructor and, if necessary, to the appropriate fire or medical facility; give your name, telephone number, and address. Tell where you will meet the emergency vehicle. If individuals are involved, report how many; whether they are unconscious, burned, or trapped; whether an explosion has occurred, and whether there is or has been a chemical or electrical fire.

(b) Tell others in the area about the nature of the emergency.

(c) Do not move any injured persons unless they are in immediate danger from chemical exposure or fire. Keep them warm. Unnecessary movement can severely complicate neck injuries and fractures.

(d) Meet the ambulance or fire crews at the place you indicated. Send someone else if you cannot go.

(e) Do not make any other telephone calls unless they directly relate to the control of the emergency.

2. Fires
2.1 Fire Prevention

The best way to fight a fire is to prevent it. Fires can be prevented and their severity considerably reduced by proper housekeeping and by thoughtful reflection about what you are doing. This includes prompt removal of waste, separation of flammable liquids from combustible material such as cardboard boxes and paper towels, storage only of limited quantities of flammable material, and unobstructed aisles and exits. Stand back, take a look, ask: "Are there any frayed wires? Is a sparking motor stirrer being used to stir a flammable liquid? Are those bottles too close to the edge of the bench? Is the work space cluttered? Do I understand each of the potential hazards in what I am about to do? Am I prepared in advance to take preventive steps?"

2.2 Dealing with a Fire

When a fire occurs, the following actions are recommended:

(a) A fire contained in a small vessel can usually be suffocated by covering the vessel. Do not pick up the vessel. Do not cover with dry towels or cloths. Remove nearby flammable materials to avoid spread of the fire.

(b) If the fire is burning over an area too large for the fire to be suffocated quickly and simply, all persons should evacuate the area except those trained and equipped to fight structural fires. Do not use elevators to leave the building; use the stairs.

(c) Activate the fire alarm. Notify co-workers and the instructor. Call the fire department. As much as possible, follow procedures that have been established and practiced.

(d) If you have been trained in the use of a fire extinguisher, fight the fire from a position from which you can escape, and only if you are confident that you will be successful. Small fires just starting often can be extinguished, but not always. If not extinguished, a fire can quickly threaten your life and that of your co-workers. Remember, it is easy to underestimate a fire.

(e) Toxic gases and smoke may be present during a fire and those persons trying to contain the fire must avoid breathing gases and smoke. These fires should be fought only by properly trained and equipped personnel.

(f) Smother fires involving very reactive metals with powdered graphite or with a fire extinguisher designed for metal fires. Carbon dioxide and the usual dry chemical fire extinguishers will intensify fires of alkali, alkaline earth, and certain other metals, including aluminum, magnesium, zirconium, hafnium, thorium and uranium.

(g) Fire fighters should be informed what chemicals are involved, or which chemicals may become involved. A current inventory list is required and a copy should be readily available outside the work area. Laboratories should be posted with the National Fire Protection Association diamond which provides much emergency information.

(h) Fire involving chemicals increase the possibility of explosions. Special care should be taken to keep fire or excessive heat from volatile solvents, compressed gas cylinders, reactive metals and explosive compounds.

(i) Immediately after the fire, all extinguishers that were used should be recharged or replaced with full ones.

2.3 Personal Injuries Involving Fires

If a person's clothing is on fire, that person should use the safety shower. If the shower is not readily available, douse the individual with water or wrap the person in a coat, blanket or whatever is available to extinguish the fire and roll the person on the floor. Fire blankets must be used with caution because wrapping the body can force flames toward the face and neck. Quickly remove any clothing contaminated with chemicals. Use caution when removing pullover shirts or sweaters to prevent contamination of the eyes. Douse with water to remove heat and place clean, wet, cold cloths on burned areas. Wrap the injured person to avoid shock and exposure. Get medical attention promptly.

3. Chemical Spills on Personnel

For spills covering small amounts of skin, immediately flush with flowing water for no less than fifteen minutes. If there is no visible burn, wash with warm water and soap, removing any jewelry to facilitate removal of any residual materials. Check the MSDS to see if any delayed effects should be expected. It is advisable to seek medical attention for even minor chemical burns.

For spills on clothes, don't attempt to wipe the clothes. Quickly remove all contaminated clothing, shoes and jewelry while using the safety shower. Seconds count, and no time should be wasted because of modesty. Be careful not to spread the chemical on the skin, or especially in the eyes. Use caution when removing pullover shirts or sweaters to prevent contamination of the eyes. It may be better to cut the garments off. Immediately flood the affected body area with tempered water for at least 15 minutes. Resume if pain returns. Do not use creams, lotions or salves. Get medical attention as soon as possible. Launder contaminated clothes separately from other clothing.

Your instructor should make certain that the medical personnel understand exactly what chemicals are involved and that medical personnel (including physicians, nurses, and paramedics) recognize and use proper treatment for that exposure. Preferably this should be done in advance of any potential emergency. The exact chemical name should be supplied. For example, exposure to hydrochloric acid is very different medically than exposure to hydrofluoric acid, yet both are sometimes simply called acids.

For splashes into the eye, immediately flush the eye with tempered potable water from a gently flowing source for at least 15 minutes. Hold the eyelids away from the eyeball, move the eye up and down and sideways to wash thoroughly behind the eyelids. An eyewash fountain should be used, but if one is not available, injured persons should be placed on their backs and water gently poured into their eyes for at least fifteen minutes. First aid must be followed by prompt treatment by a member of a medical staff or an ophthalmologist especially alerted and acquainted with chemical injuries.

4. Other Accidents Involving Personal Injury

Anyone overcome with smoke or fumes should be removed to uncontaminated air and treated for shock. Remember to evaluate the possibility of harm to the rescuer before entering or continuing to remain in a toxic environment. If hazardous chemicals are ingested, follow the first aid treatment shown on the label or in the material safety data sheet. Never give anything by mouth to an unconscious person. Attempt to learn exactly what substances were ingested and inform the medical staff (while the victim is *en route* to a hospital, if possible). The nearest poison control center can give advice.

If the injured person is not breathing, provide mouth-to-mouth resuscitation. The following procedure is recommended: Place the victim on his/her back on a smooth hard surface, clean the mouth of any obstruction and loosen tight clothing. Place the palm of one hand on the victim's forehead. With the other hand, lift the victim's chin and tilt the head back so that the chin is pointing upward. Pinch the victim's nose to prevent leakage and blow through the victim's mouth (a good seal is important) with sufficient force to make the chest expand. If the victim's chest does not expand, recheck the mouth for any obstruction, reposition the head and resume blowing into the mouth (once again making a good seal). After two successful breaths separated by four to five seconds, check the carotid artery for a pulse. If none is found, administer cardiopulmonary resuscitation (CPR).

If an individual is bleeding severely, control the bleeding by compressing the wound with a cloth or whatever is available. Elevate the injury above the level of the heart. If blood is spurting, place a pad directly on the cut and apply firm pressure. Wrap the injured person to avoid shock and get immediate medical attention. In the case of a less severe cut, wash the cut and remove any pieces of glass, wrap the injured person to avoid shock (except in case of a trivial cut) and get medical attention. A pressure pad should be applied firmly on the wound. Tourniquets should be used only by persons trained in first aid.

Do not touch a person in contact with a live electrical circuit. Disconnect the power first or the rescuer may be seriously injured.

5. Chemical Spills

All spills should be cleaned up promptly, efficiently and properly. Appropriately warn all individuals at risk of involvement. Not only will they be spared exposure to the hazard, but also the spread of the hazard will be minimized. For chemical spills on the skin or in the eyes, treatment must begin immediately. Often the volume spilled is not so important as the toxicity of the substance. Therefore, local procedures should be established and followed for determining when evacuation is necessary and whether laboratory personnel or an emergency spill control team should conduct the cleanup.

Containing the spill rapidly is a primary concern, because the smaller the area involved, the easier the cleanup. Diking of liquids by surrounding the involved area with an absorbent retaining material is recommended. After the spill has been contained, it can be cleaned up with appropriate materials. Commercially available or homemade spill control kits can be useful here.

If there is no fire hazard and the material is not believed to be volatile or toxic, clean it up as directed by the instructor. Refer to the appropriate material safety data sheet. To facilitate cleaning up liquids, use an absorbent material that will neutralize the liquids if possible (trisodium phosphate, sand followed by sodium bicarbonate solution or powder for acids, sodium thiosulfate solution for bromine, *etc.*). Commercial absorbents (*e.g.*, Oil-Dri and Zorb-All), vermiculite, or small particles (about 30 mesh) of Kitty Litter or other satisfactory clay absorbents can be used. Dry sand is less effective. A dustpan and brush should be used, and protective gloves should be worn. While wearing gloves, clean the contaminated area with soap and water and mop it dry. If the spill is on the floor, some absorbent should be sprinkled on the spot to prevent slipping. Note that vermiculite and some other absorbents create a slipping hazard when wet.

If a volatile, flammable or toxic material is spilled, immediately warn everyone to extinguish flames and turn off spark producing equipment such as brush type motors. Shut down all equipment and leave the area until it is decontaminated. Clothing contaminated by spills or splashes should be immediately removed to prevent skin penetration. The instructor will be responsible for designating the extent of evacuation and the proper cleanup procedure. During the cleanup, the designated persons will avoid skin contact, and, to prevent inhalation, wear appropriate breathing apparatus.

Many small liquid spills (<100 mL) can be absorbed with paper towels, sand, or an absorbent. However, paper towels can increase the surface area and evaporation, increasing the fire hazard. Most spills of solids can be brushed up and disposed of in appropriate solid waste containers, but care must be exercised to avoid reactive combinations. Don't leave paper towels or other materials used to clean up a spill in open trash cans in the work area.

After cleanup, all materials, including paper towels used in the cleanup, must be disposed of as wastes. Be particularly careful that flammable liquids absorbed during cleanup do not present an absorbent fire hazard.

Overview for Faculty and Administrators

Responsibility for Safety

The faculty and staff of the chemistry or science department are responsible for the administration of the safety program. All individuals must participate in appropriate training programs and are responsible for performing their jobs safely. Untrained students or visitors should not be permitted to work with chemicals. A laboratory instructor should be responsible for no more than twenty-five students at one time for the safest laboratory programs. The instructor should be in the laboratory for the entire laboratory period for high school or college undergraduate level courses.

Every instructor or laboratory supervisor must:

(a) Set a good example by
- observing all rules and recommendations,
- wearing protective equipment where recommended, and
- being enthusiastic about safety.

(b) Conduct appropriate safety and evacuation drills on a regular basis.

(c) Be alert for unsafe conditions.

(d) Conduct frequent and thorough inspections.

(e) Take effective corrective action promptly.

(f) Maintain discipline and enforce rules.

(g) Assume responsibility for visitors and require that they follow the same rules as other laboratory workers and are escorted or supervised at all times.

(h) Ensure that the faculty, students and staff have access to and understand the information on the appropriate MSDSs.

(i) Carefully review all procedures for possible health, safety and environmental problems before the work is begun. Review the relevant MSDSs before starting any laboratory procedures.

(j) Be familiar with a file of publications on chemical safety, which is readily available to faculty, staff, students and visitors, and encourage its use.

In addition to a growing awareness of the need for adequate safety precautions and training, there has also been increased recognition of the health effects of prolonged, low level exposure to many chemicals. However, the latter subject is beyond the purpose and scope of this manual and the reader is urged to seek specific guidance from appropriate federal and state agencies and specialized textbooks in this field. Appendix II contains a bibliography of journal articles, books, and online databases; Appendix V gives organizations which should be contacted for additional safety information. Finally, Appendix VI lists addresses and telephone numbers of federal offices including Occupational Safety and Health Administration (OSHA) Regional Offices and the regional offices of the Environmental Protection Agency.

Safety Officers and Safety Committees

Experience has shown that effective safety programs require a firm commitment at the highest administrative level. A safety officer should be appointed with the primary responsibility to advise and assist administrators, faculty and staff in the area of safety and health. The safety officer's position should be a recognized part of workload and not assigned as an overload responsibility. This individual may also function as the emergency coordinator.

A safety committee should be formed that includes members from the major divisions of the chemistry or science department. The committee should include permanent members from the administration, such as the safety officer. The safety committee should be organized to advise and assist administrators, lab supervisors, students and workers, but it should not be responsible for working conditions and practices.

The committee should set up and supervise a monthly safety inspection of the laboratory facilities, including unoccupied areas and storerooms. Hazardous conditions should be reported and corrected. Use of a serial number and date for each hazardous condition reported is helpful in keeping track of such conditions until they can be corrected. In practice, a revolving inspection team is preferable because this brings the judgment of more individuals into the system. The person responsible for an area in which a hazard is identified should be formally advised of the hazard and be given suggestions for correction. After corrective measures have been completed, the person responsible should report to the committee chairman. Periodically the chairman should review past reports for recurrent hazards and institute recommendations and actions to eliminate them, consulting with the faculty and others for suggestions. Appendix VII contains a sample inspection checklist.

Safety Rules for the Chemical Laboratory

Under OSHA Hazard Communication regulations, a specific set of safety rules must be developed and communicated clearly to all employees. Although non-employee students are not covered by these regulations, each student should attest by signature that he or she has read and understands the safety rules. These rules must be rigorously and impartially enforced. Willful noncompliance should result in dismissal or suspension from the laboratory.

The following are suggested as rules for persons in all chemical laboratories:

(a) Always wear proper eye protection in chemical work, handling and storage areas. Contact lenses should normally not be worn. Fitted goggles are essential if, for therapeutic reasons, contact lenses must be worn.

(b) Always know the hazards and physical and chemical properties of the materials used (*e.g.*, corrosivity, flammability, reactivity, and toxicity).

(c) Always wear appropriate protective clothing.

(d) Confine long hair and loose clothing. Do not wear high-heeled shoes, open-toed shoes, sandals or shoes made of woven material.

Do not wear shorts, cutoffs or miniskirts.

(e) Always wash hands and arms with soap and water before leaving the work area. This applies even if one has been wearing gloves.

(f) Never perform any work when alone in the chemical laboratory. At least two people must be present and undergraduate students must be supervised by an instructor at all times.

(g) Never eat, drink, smoke or apply cosmetics in areas where chemicals are used or stored.

(h) Never perform unauthorized work, preparations or experiments.

(i) Never engage in horseplay, pranks or other acts of mischief in chemical work areas.

(j) Never remove chemicals from the facility without proper authorization.

Preparation for Medical Emergencies

This manual addresses minimal specific first aid treatment. Proper handling techniques are discussed, as well as symptoms of overexposure to certain selected chemicals. The authors strongly recommend that for all chemicals used in the laboratory, both the MSDSs and competent medical authorities be consulted regarding first aid treatment.

In planning for potential emergencies, consult with local emergency personnel in advance and establish plans for the handling of chemical emergencies. At a minimum, make the following preparations:

(a) Always have first aid equipment readily available.

(b) Prominently post the location and phone numbers of the local physicians qualified to handle chemical emergency cases and of local medical facilities. Also post the telephone number of the local poison control center.

(c) Train sufficient staff in basic first aid and cardiopulmonary resuscitation (CPR). Red Cross certification or its equivalent should be encouraged for all personnel. Contact the local Red Cross chapter for information about appropriate training modules.

(d) Make arrangements to ensure that someone knowledgeable about the accident always accompanies the injured person to medical assistance and that a copy of the MSDS for the chemical(s) involved go with the victim if at all possible.

(e) Establish procedures to ensure that following any first aid, only a nurse or physician qualified to handle chemical emergencies provide further examination and treatment.

There are other preparations to be made in advance for medical handling of emergencies involving laboratory chemicals. For example, if first aid treatment is not described in the MSDS, a recommended practice is to add this information to the MSDS without delay. Examples of emergencies that one should anticipate are

- thermal, cryogenic and chemical burns
- cuts and puncture wounds from glass or metal that is contaminated with chemicals
- chemicals (liquid, dust, glass) in the eye
- skin irritation by chemicals

- poisoning by ingestion, inhalation, skin absorption, or injection
- asphyxiation (chemical or electrical)
- lachrymatory vapor irritation

Accident Reporting

All accidents should be reported. Accidents resulting in even minor medical treatment or observation must be recorded. A formal, written report, stating the causes and consequences of each accident should be made to the designated authorities including the insurance carrier. Recommendations for the prevention of recurrences should be discussed with the safety officer.

A written report of each accident should be submitted to the administration and to the safety officer, who should take appropriate measures to prevent recurrence. A periodic review of accident reports will often reveal problem areas that need special attention. There are certain OSHA reporting requirements which may apply depending on the institution and the nature of the accident. Unusual or unexplainable chemical accidents should be reported in the Letters to the Editor column of *Chemical & Engineering News* to alert others.

Safety Training

Responsibility for Training

Academic institutions have the moral and professional responsibility to train students in safe laboratory practices even if this training is not legally required. The institution is responsible for the training not only of the students who are taking the various laboratory courses, and of the assistants provided by the department, but also for other employees working with or exposed to chemicals. Students are expected to adhere to all safety rules and to participate conscientiously in any training exercises. Furthermore, students have the responsibility to seek advice and guidance whenever they are in doubt about safety procedures or potential hazards in their laboratory work.

Instruction should be given to students and staff members regarding hazards of the chemical being used in a particular course and the manner in which these chemicals are to be handled and disposed of safely. The information provided by the references in Appendix II and on the labels and material safety data sheets should be understood.

Evacuation and Fire Drills

Each student should know the location of the fire exits, alarms (and their operation), and telephones available during regular school hours as well as after hours. Instruction in fire drills should be scheduled on a regular basis (at least annually or as otherwise specified by local regulations).

Use of Fire Extinguishers

Each faculty and staff member associated with a particular laboratory must know the location of fire extinguishers and be trained annually in the proper method of operating them. Persons without the necessary hands-on training should not be permitted to operate a fire extinguisher.

Safety Showers and Eye Washes
Every student should know the location of the nearest safety shower and eye wash and how to operate them.

Material Safety Data Sheets (MSDSs)

As required by the Hazard Communication Standard, an OSHA regulation found in 29 CFR 1910.1200, and as required by similar regulations in some states, material safety data sheets are references to be used principally for the training of workers concerning the hazards and precautionary measures applicable to those particular chemicals that workers will handle in the workplace. Refer to the detailed discussion of material safety data sheets in Section III.

OSHA requires that, for every hazardous chemical on the premises, a MSDS be readily available for employees' perusal. Because there is some level of hazard associated with every chemical, OSHA generally interprets *all* chemicals as hazardous. OSHA imposes no restriction on the sources of the material safety data sheets that are made available to the workers, but it does require all suppliers of hazardous chemicals to furnish copies of material safety data sheets to their customers. Therefore, this is the usual source of MSDSs for the employers' workers. In some states, the MSDS must be from the supplier to fulfill the state legal requirements.

A MSDS also describes other hazardous characteristics of a chemical or mixture. Thus, if a chemical can be absorbed through the intact skin, the MSDS will so state and will also prescribe the use of protective equipment, such as gloves or full protective clothing, as appropriate. If the MSDS does not describe the material (*e.g.*, rubber, neoprene, or polyethylene, for gloves) the supplier may be able to suggest a suitable material.

Known and anticipated carcinogens recognized as such by competent authorities *must* be identified in MSDSs. But, there is as yet no corresponding recognized basis of authority for the identification of mutagens (substances capable of causing permanent, transmissible alterations in the genetic coding) or teratogens (agents interfering with normal prenatal development causing abnormalities in the fetus). Hence, a MSDS may be silent concerning mutagenic, teratogenic, neurotoxic or nephrotic hazards due to lack of information.

OSHA has prepared a suggested format for a MSDS, but any format that supplies the OSHA required information is acceptable. This includes information stored in a computer database provided that the information can be accessed readily. The principal parts required in a MSDS include physical data, fire and explosion hazards, toxicity hazards, other health hazards, propensity to react vigorously (often called an incompatible chemicals or reactivity list), spill and leak cleanup procedures, and above all, precautionary measures which, if taken, will materially reduce the probability of harm when the chemical is used. Therefore, when properly prepared, a MSDS is a useful tool in the training of users, including students, who will use that chemical in their laboratory work. Note that although OSHA has no authority to require the training of students concerning hazardous chemicals, faculty can take advantage of the availability of the MSDSs that are furnished by chemical suppliers and use these in the training of students concerning chemical safety and health hazards and precautions.

A MSDS is always a tertiary source of information and not all MSDSs are prepared from reliable sources. Therefore, some MSDSs are less accurately informative than others. Not all fully describe the known hazardous properties of the substance, and some describe hazards that are not attributable to that chemical. It is often useful to compare MSDSs from different suppliers for the same chemical. Better yet, refer to the primary literature, or, because this is often difficult to obtain, refer to reliable review sources, such as the NIOSH/OSHA Occupational Health Guidelines, the books by Patty, Gosselin, and Bretherick, or the NIOSH (National Institute for Occupational Safety and Health) Criteria Documents.

Before relying on a MSDS as an educational resource, an instructor should examine the contents carefully for omissions, inaccurate statements, and internal inconsistencies. There are currently efforts to improve and standardize the quality and accuracy of the information in material safety data sheets. Some of the typical errors found in current MSDSs include:

(a) No identification of the "target organs", *e.g.* liver, kidney, lungs, central nervous system, or other organ(s) or organ system(s), that are threatened by the chemical when it is improperly handled.

(b) Incomplete PEL statement. For example, the MSDS may state that the PEL is 100 ppm, but a quick look at the current 29 CFR 1910.1000 (which should be available in every chemistry department), clearly indicates that the PEL includes an excursion limit of 300 ppm. The correct MSDS information would include both limits, the time weighted average of 100 ppm and the excursion limit of 300 ppm.

(c) A statement that the percent volatile is "nil" or "not available" coupled with the statement in a different location in the same MSDS that the vapor pressure is 20 mm at 70° F.

(d) A statement that the chemical is not flammable, coupled with the statement that to fight fires, one should use carbon dioxide or another fire extinguishing agent when that chemical is burning.

(e) For a chemical that is altered in the heat of a fire and forms toxic products, a statement that such products *may* be toxic when the correct word is *will* be toxic.

(f) A description of certain consequences following overexposure with no explanation of the criteria by which an exposure is to be identified as an "overexposure".

(g) A statement in one section that overexposure *might* cause a certain adverse effect, compared to a contradictory statement in another section that overexposure *will* cause those results.

(h) A recommendation to wear "impervious" gloves or other clothing, but no description of what materials are, in fact, impervious to the chemical. Note that even so called impervious materials will resist penetration for only a few hours, at most.

(i) First aid procedures that instruct one not to administer any liquids to an unconscious person but fail to instruct what to do when the victim is unconscious.

(j) Statements to keep a chemical away from ignition sources without either specifying that the vapors can travel hundreds of feet or otherwise indicating conditions that determine safe distances.

(k) Statements recommending that a chemical be used only with adequate ventilation coupled with silence on the definition of adequate ventilation. Adequate ventilation is ventilation sufficient to maintain the concentration of vapors in the user's breathing air below the PEL or TLV, provided that the vapor concentration is determined by quantitative measurements.

(l) Disclaimer statements, that say, in effect: The information contained herein is based upon information believed to be reliable. However, we cannot guarantee that any of it is, in fact, correct.

Material safety data sheets can provide unique opportunities for students to gain insight into how practical decisions are made when the use of a chemical is being considered. MSDS sections on toxicity and precautions guide faculty in determining the selection of one chemical for student use in place of another that, chemically, would work well in a particular experiment; *e.g.*, the substitution of slightly toxic strontium chloride for the very toxic barium chloride in the laboratory study of insoluble sulfates. Similarly, a MSDS section on the reactivity of acetic acid with potassium permanganate or other oxidizer reminds faculty to limit the amounts to be used by students in an experimental investigation.

Material safety data sheets should be available to students, faculty and staff. Hazard and precautionary information from MSDSs should be incorporated as part of all laboratory procedures. Student laboratory reports should include safety and health concerns, the management of hazardous situations, and where appropriate, the proper disposal of both products and left-over reagents. Students should be encouraged to understand that the practical information found in the reactivity section of a MSDS is very important in designing safe experimental procedures. It is important for academic institutions to involve material safety data sheets in all aspects of laboratory work. It is equally important to instruct students so that later, after graduation, they, and those whom they supervise, will handle chemicals safely.

Personal Protective Equipment

Protective Clothing

Aprons, lab coats, gloves, and other protective clothing, preferably made of chemically inert material, should be readily available and used. Appendix I compares the properties of a number of different clothing materials. Note that most lab coats and aprons are made of substances that will burn. Experiments or processes involving corrosive or reactive materials, such as strong acids or bases, require use of goggles and perhaps face shields. Gloves must provide sufficient arm protection to minimize the chance of spilled chemicals making contact with the skin. Examine the manufacturers' claims and test data carefully and use the gloves only under the conditions and with the chemicals for which they are intended.

Protection for legs and feet should be provided by lab coat or apron, and shoes, and in some cases, boots.

Respirators (Self-Contained Breathing Apparatus)

At least two 30-minute OSHA approved self-contained breathing devices (not canister or filter gas masks) are required for emergency control where high concentrations of toxic vapors, gases, smoke or oxygen deficient atmospheres are frequently or potentially present. The respirators should be set in permanent cabinets outside of the danger area. Training and practice in the use and limitations of all of these devices must be given to those expected to use them. See ANSI Z 88.2-1980, *Practices for Respiratory Protection*, and refer to the OSHA regulations.

Hearing Conservation (Ear Protection)

Hearing conservation should be practiced through proper design of equipment, modifications of existing sources of noise, and the use of ear protection.

OSHA allowable occupational noise exposure limits contained in 29 CFR 1926.52 are in Table I.

Table I
OSHA Occupational Noise Exposure Limits

Duration per day, hours	Sound Level dBA slow response	
8	90	
6	92	decibels when
4	95	measured on
3	97	the A-Scale of a
2	100	standard sound
1.5	102	level meter at
1	105	slow response.
.5	110	
.25 or less	115	

Exposure to impact noise should not exceed 140 dB peak sound pressure level.

Ear protection includes earmuffs and earplugs. Generally, earmuffs have a greater attenuation factor than earplugs.

Eye Protection

The use of proper eye protection is a minimum requirement for everyone who enters a chemical work area. The type of eye protection needed depends on the circumstances. There is always a danger of splashing chemicals or flying particles. Therefore, goggles or other forms of eye protection that protect both the front and sides of the eyes are mandatory. Side shields offer some protection from objects that approach from the side, but do not provide adequate protection from chemical splashes, which can drip behind glasses. Face shields and goggles may be appropriate when working with glassware under reduced or elevated pressure and with glass apparatus used in combustion or other high-temperature operations. Face shields alone are not considered adequate eye protection according to ANSI Z 87.1-1989 and must be used in conjunction with other eye protection. Goggles should be worn when working with compressed gases.

Normally, contact lenses should not be worn in the chemistry laboratory or workplace and they are never a substitute for eye protection. If contact lenses are permitted, fitted goggles must also be worn at all times. Gases and vapors can concentrate under the lenses and cause permanent eye damage. Soft contact lenses may pose an even greater hazard than hard contact lenses in this regard. Contact lenses can also trap particulate foreign matter in the eye and thereby produce abrasion of the cornea. Further, in the event of a chemical splash into an eye, capillary action tends to hold the offending substance under the contact lens and against the surface of the cornea. At the same time, the removal of the contact lens to achieve immediate irrigation is made nearly impossible by involuntary spasm of the eyelid. Persons attempting to irrigate the eyes of an unconscious victim may be unaware that contact lenses are in place, thereby reducing the effectiveness of the wash.

A U. S. Food and Drug Administration (FDA) regulation requires that all eyeglass and sunglass lenses sold to the general public be of shatter resistant material. Although this regulation improves the protection to the general public, such eyeglasses cannot be considered adequate for laboratories and shops, which require industrial quality eye protective devices. ANSI Z 87.1-1989, *Practice for Occupational Safety and Educational Eye and Face Protection,* requirements should be considered the minimum protection. The ANSI standard requires hardened glass or plastic lenses with a minimum thickness of three mm, lens retaining, nonflammable frames, and other attributes not covered by the FDA regulation.

Considerable discomfort and damage to the eye can result from exposure to UV light. Absorption of this radiation by the outer layers of the eye (cornea and conjunctiva) produces conjunctivitis. Protective glasses should be worn by all personnel whenever they may be exposed to erythemically effective radiation. Use of lasers requires special care.

Facilities

General

All chemical laboratories and any other chemical work areas should be provided with safety showers, eyewash fountains, appropriate fire extinguishers, adequate ventilation, wash sinks, and approved waste disposal facilities. All of these should be conveniently located, properly maintained, and frequently tested. There should be two or more well-marked and unobstructed exits for evacuating the laboratory. Aisles and exits must be kept clear at all times. Special consideration should be given to ensure accessibility to safety equipment by, as well as ease of evacuation of, physically disabled individuals.

Safety equipment, such as showers, fire extinguishers, and unrestricted telephones should be readily available, located strategically, in working order and known to all. Emergency telephone numbers must be clearly posted. If an outside line is posted, include all necessary access numbers. Suggested numbers include those on the inside front cover of this manual.

Highly visible signs, temporary or permanent as appropriate, should be posted in areas where hazardous operations are being carried out or where toxic, reactive, or highly flammable chemicals are being used. It should be emphasized to all laboratory workers that before using flame, spark-producing or hot surface equipment such as motors, hot plates, and open heaters, it is crucial to verify that no flammable vapors are in the area. The turning on of a light or the ringing of a telephone has ignited flammable vapors.

Storage of chemicals in laboratories should be minimized. Suitable stockroom or chemical storage space should be used. Fume hoods used for chemical operations should never be used for the storage of chemicals. National Fire Protection Association (NFPA) *Fire Protection for Laboratories Using Chemicals: NFPA 45*, gives maximum quantities of flammable and combustible liquids that may be stored in laboratories as well as maximum container sizes. See Appendix IV.

A general alarm system, which alerts facility emergency and security services, should be provided. Automatic smoke and fire alarms are highly recommended and, in some cases, legally required, especially in the absence of automatic water sprinklers. Such systems must be properly maintained and monitored, and the results documented on a regular basis to ensure their proper operation.

Emergency drills are essential. In case of general evacuation, students, faculty and staff should be required to go to a designated safe area outside the building and remain there until accounted for. Discussions with local fire officials should be held to review the special problems of fire containment and handling in the chemical work environment and may be mandated by law if the facility must comply with the requirements of Title III of the Superfund Appropriation and Reauthorization Act (SARA).

Laboratory Ventilation

It is recognized that in many academic institutions the laboratory experience is partially conducted on laboratory benches and not in laboratory hoods. Therefore, it is important to characterize the limits of available room ventilation. Safety and ventilation professionals can help identify the rate at which toxic materials leave the laboratory atmosphere. Laboratory air must not be recirculated, because this practice will return and concentrate vapors in the system. Many laboratory instructors are changing to smaller or microscale experiments to minimize unpleasant or toxic materials in the laboratory atmosphere.

Fume Hoods

One key to safe handling of chemicals in enclosed areas is a good, properly installed hood system. The design of an effective ventilating system is a complicated problem well beyond the scope of this manual. Architects and engineers require such references as the current edition of *Industrial Ventilation* by the American Conference of Governmental Industrial Hygienists when developing new facilities. A useful reference by G. T. Saunders aimed at improving the atmosphere in older laboratories is available in the *Journal of Chemical Education*. Additionally, the National Academy of Sciences' report, *Prudent Practices for Handling Hazardous*

Chemicals in Laboratories, and Young's *Improving Safety in the Chemical Laboratory* provide extensive discussions of laboratory ventilation problems. An article by G. Thomas Saunders in the *Journal of Chemical Education* addresses hood requirements in academic institutions. Refer to Appendix II for additional references.

Operations where flammable gases, toxic vapors, or noxious odors are given off should be performed in fume hoods. The now recognized potential for long-term physiological harm from substances that are not acutely hazardous requires greater effort to minimize contact with airborne toxic substances by appropriate standards for laboratory ventilation and by enforced good practices in the use of fume hoods. *Prudent Practices for Handling Hazardous Chemicals in Laboratories* recommends that in a laboratory where workers spend most of their time working with chemicals, there should be a hood for each two workers and each worker should have at least 2.5 linear feet of working space at the hood face.

Fume hoods must operate properly. The exhaust rate is not a reliable single measure of hood performance because air supply to the room and drafts across the hood face alter the hood's effectiveness. A higher exhaust rate than is needed for protection is uneconomical, and such rates can cause turbulence and degrade the hood's performance. Specifications on exhaust rates are not by themselves acceptable measures of hood performance. Uniform face velocities as low as 60 feet per minute (fpm) in ideal systems with enforced good work practices may prove adequate. Systems less well designed may benefit from higher exhaust rates, perhaps 70-120 fpm, but rates as high as 150 fpm will worsen the protection as turbulence increases and causes spillage from the hood. Actual containment tests of installed hoods under conditions of use are strongly recommended. See ANSI/ASHRAE (American National Standards Institute/ American Society of Heating, Refrigerating and Air-Conditioning Engineers) 110-1985 for specific details of installation and containment testing.

Periodic inspections should be made to determine the condition of the hood and to check for proper functioning of the ducts and exhaust system. Velometers should be used to survey hoods on a regular schedule, at least semi-annually, to ensure uniformity of air flow over the face of the hood and to detect any changes. Fans should be located on the building roof so that all ductwork in the building is under negative pressure. The incoming supply air must be adequate to meet the exhaust air requirements, and there should be no circulation of exhaust air from fume hoods back into the laboratory building.

Canopy style hoods at a bench top normally do not provide acceptable protection because of the difficulty of attaining airflow balance and appropriate exhaust rates. Bench-top canopy hoods can fit some special needs where the work in progress can be kept essentially within the hood by the use of flexible ductwork (elephant trunks).

Good work practices are essential in the use of hoods. Refer to the article, *Good Practices for Hood Use* by Mikell and Drinkard (1984) and the article by Mikell and Fuller in the February, 1988, issue of the *Journal of Chemical Education.* Hoods should never be used to store chemicals or apparatus. Always have an emergency plan in the possible event of hood failure.

Sinks

The water supply for laboratory sinks must be separate from that used for toilets, drinking water and emergency showers or eye washes. This is necessary to prevent possible contamination of the potable water supply. Back siphonage or back pressure can suck sink water into the potable water system through hoses or other apparatus. Building codes require a check valve system that must be tested periodically. It is advantageous to separate laboratory sink drainage from the sanitary drainage in order to facilitate independent treatment of each type of waste where this is appropriate.

Safety Showers

Each laboratory area must be equipped with a safety shower. ANSI Z 358.1-1981, *Emergency Eyewash and Shower Equipment,* requires that emergency showers should be located no more than 10 seconds in time nor greater than 100 feet in distance from the hazard. The shower area must be readily accessible, be kept clear of obstructions, and be clearly labeled. Chain pulls to activate the shower are difficult to grasp in an emergency, and should be provided with a large ring. The valve should open readily and remain open until intentionally closed. Water flow must be sufficient to drench the subject rapidly and to accommodate more than one person. ANSI Z 358.1-1981 requires a minimum flow of 113.6 liters per minute (30 gallons per minute) of water. Tempered, potable water should be used in safety showers. Although an associated floor drain is desirable, its absence should not prohibit installation of a safety shower. The shower should be tested on a regular basis and a record kept of such tests.

Eyewash Fountains

Eyewash fountains should provide a copious and gentle flow of tempered aerated potable water for a period of at least 15 minutes (15 minutes of cold water is intolerable). Plumbed installations are best and strongly recommended. When possible, students should be encouraged to practice the procedure. Use of the hands should not be required to maintain the water flow.

Eyewash fountains should be tested on a regular basis and a record kept of such tests. The National Safety Council recommends a three minute flush of plumbed installations weekly to reduce the threat of eye infections. ANSI Z 358.1-1981 requires that eyewash units be located no more than 10 seconds in time nor greater than 100 feet in distance from the hazard. Their location should be clearly labeled.

A hand-held eye wash spray with a 5-ft hose is more adaptable than fixed fountains for unusual situations, including head and body splashes. Portable eyewash units provide an inadequate supply of water, require strict attention to maintenance, and may provide an environment for the growth of microorganisms. Their use should be discouraged except as an interim wash until the injured party can reach a plumbed fixture.

Fire Extinguishers

Fire extinguishers in the laboratory should be the appropriate type for the expected fire emergency and be capable of rapid use. Dry chemical fire extinguishers may be preferred for certain areas, but carbon dioxide is satisfactory for most small fires (with the notable exception of fires of alkali, alkaline earth and certain other metals) and is cleaner to use around most equipment. Conventional dry chemical extinguishers expel a stream of sodium or potassium bicarbonate powder and are not recommended for Class A fires (wood, paper). Multipurpose dry chemical extinguishers release a stream of monoammonium phosphate and are often preferred. The newer agents such as Halon 1301 and 2404 may be useful in certain installations such as electronic instrument and computer areas, but in a fire, some Halon extinguishing agents may produce toxic gases. All faculty and staff and selected students should be trained in the use of fire extinguishers.

Electrical Hazards

All electrical outlets must have a grounding connection requiring a three-pronged plug. This is required under OSHA regulations. If equipment does not have a three-pronged plug, replace the plug and cord to ground the equipment properly. All electrical outlets should be protected by ground-fault interrupters, but note that ground-fault interrupters do not work in two-wire installations.

Polarity of outlet wiring and continuity of grounding connections, including leads to the building ground itself, should be checked regularly by an authorized inspector. The *National Electrical Code* should be followed in all installations. This includes proper grounding as well as proper equipment for hazardous areas.

Eliminate wiring that is frayed or worn or stretched across the floor where someone could trip over it. Eliminate obstructed switch gear and panel boards, unlabeled panel boards, electrical outlets with open (or missing) cover plates, and excessive use of extension cords. The condition of wiring, plugs, cords, and related equipment should be frequently inspected.

All personnel should know the location of circuit breakers and how to cut off all electrical service in case of fire or accident. All circuit breakers should be labeled properly.

Storage and Inventory Management

Safe storage and transportation of chemicals should be provided. Adequate security to prevent unauthorized access must be assured. Housekeeping in the storage area must be neat and orderly. Storage facilities and equipment must be stable and secure against sliding and collapse, and not subject to flooding. Make sure that shelf units are stable and in no danger of tilting. In regions subject to earthquakes, restraints should be installed on every shelf. Storage for large containers of reagents should be provided on a low shelf, preferably in a tray adequate to contain spills or leakage. Containers of chemicals should never be stored on the floor, even temporarily. For additional protection for the eyes, corrosives should never be stored above eye level.

Keep only minimum quantities of flammable liquids in the workplace as described by OSHA regulations and NFPA 45, *Fire Protection for Laboratories Using Chemicals*. Store larger quantities in approved safety containers or in fire-resistant properly ventilated solvent cabinets away from ignition sources. Maintain laboratory storage for current work only. Large amounts of flammable liquids should be stored in a separate storage building with an automatic fire extinguishing system.

Storage of chemicals in household refrigerators constitutes a unique hazard because the various control switches and defroster heaters can spark and ignite flammable materials. Explosions and fires may occur. Domestic (household-type) refrigerators should never be used for chemical storage. Most household refrigerators can be modified by a trained technician to remove internal sources of spark. However, the motor and other electrical parts on the exterior of a modified domestic refrigerator can still ignite flammable vapors leaking out of the refrigerator or already in the room. In so-called explosion proof refrigerators, the internal wiring has been modified to eliminate ignition sources and the external motor and switches are sealed.

Many chemicals deteriorate with storage time. Keep all stored chemicals, especially flammable liquids, away from heat and direct sunlight. Peroxide forming chemicals deserve special considerations at all times and particularly in storage. Peroxide formation is accelerated by the presence of UV light and elevated temperature. Careful records of the storage history of compounds that form peroxides on standing should be maintained and periodically reviewed.

Chemical manufacturers occasionally list an expiration date for a given chemical such as isopropyl ether and indicate specific storage precautions. A definite date is stamped on the bottle or can, and precautions and disposal instructions are provided. However, manufacturer-supplied expiration dates are the exception and not the rule.

Chemists recognize that chemicals cannot be stored indefinitely and that storage guidelines must be established. Although the deterioration in storage of a specific compound cannot be predicted in detail, one can often generalize about the reaction characteristics of groups of compounds. Then some general conclusions about the stability of classes of chemicals can be reached and some corresponding storage time spans can be identified.

It is recommended that the date of receipt and the date of initial opening of every chemical container be indicated on its label. For the purposes of chemical storage, decision dates are more useful than expiration dates. When stored chemicals have reached their decision date, they are removed and a decision is made either to extend the storage period or to dispose of the chemical. A simple color coding system can identify the decision dates on the containers. The principal criteria for assigning time spans to chemicals are the conditions in storage, the rates at which the compounds are oxidized by oxygen, the rates at which the compounds react with moisture, and, in some cases, the ways in which they may polymerize. The lifetime of the container might also be considered. Chemicals that have been stored for a long period of time (perhaps five years) should be examined for disposal.

The reaction of compounds with air or moisture can produce products that are hazardous, *e.g.*, explosive or toxic. Alternatively, the quality of the compound can be significantly reduced so that it becomes essentially worthless. If there is a reasonable possibility that a class of compounds degrades rapidly, the decision date should involve a short time span. When the decision dates of stored chemicals have been reached, the chemicals are removed from the shelf and a chemist either overrides the decision date and sends the compound back to the storage shelf with a new decision date or disposes of the chemical. Visual inspection of stored chemicals is important in the disposal decision. Indications for disposal of chemicals include the following:

- Slightly cloudy liquids
- Chemicals that are changing color *e.g.*, darkening
- Spotting on solids
- Caking of anhydrous materials
- Existence of solids in liquids or liquids in solids
- Pressure buildup in bottles
- Evidence of reaction with water
- Damage to the container

A chemical inventory management program involves a realistic appraisal of chemicals required to conduct a viable chemistry program, an understanding of the incompatibility of chemicals, a reasonable method of identification of chemicals for disposal, a proper disposal strategy which includes labeling and monitoring, a clear understanding of the available storage space, and a qualitative risk assessment of placing the chemicals into the available space.

The first step is to reduce the number and amounts of chemicals that need to be stored to an absolute minimum. This will require special coordination with faculty and staff, so that chemical inventories might be shared. The next step is to classify the chemicals into chemical groups with the help of publications such as ASTM P168, the *Proposed Guide for Estimating the Incompatibility of Selected Hazardous Wastes Based on Binary Chemical Reactions* to guide difficult decisions. If only a very few chemicals in a particular hazard class are used, it may be expedient to purchase those chemicals as they are needed. If they could be removed from the storage facility, the storage problems would be simplified. The next step is to match the identified groups against the storage space available. Ideally, each group should be placed in a separate area, but often this is not possible. Many publications can offer help in describing the reactions between groups. Especially recommended is Bretherick's *Handbook of Reactive Chemical Hazards*. Some groups react and produce an explosion, while others generate heat, fire, toxic or flammable gases. Other groups do not react at all with each other. The storage area must be adequate to separate the most reactive groups.

Another storage problem is presented by chemical wastes which are being held for subsequent disposal or treatment. They must be stored in a proper storage area. This storage area must have adequate ventilation and provisions for dealing with accidents such as fires, spills or container leaks. There must be sufficient room for safe storage of incompatible materials. If wastes are to be held for more than 90 days, a storage facility permit must be obtained from the EPA.

Labeling

ANSI Z 129.1-1988, *Standard for Hazardous Industrial Chemicals— Precautionary Labeling*, should be consulted. The OSHA booklet 3084,

Chemical Hazard Communication, summarizes the federal regulatory requirements for the labeling of containers in the workplace. Because state regulations may vary, they should also be consulted.

All chemicals received should be labeled with the date received, the date of initial opening, and the decision date for the chemical. Chemicals that are repackaged should have secure, waterproof labels, marked with waterproof ink, that contain information about hazards and precautions as well as name, date packaged, and strength or purity.

Waste Disposal

In the United States, disposal of certain chemical wastes is governed by the Resource Conservation and Recovery Act (RCRA) of 1976, as amended from time to time. For some states and local jurisdictions, related and often more restrictive requirements also apply. A material is defined as a waste at the point that it is determined that the material is no longer to be used and it is time to discard it.

The following remarks summarize the requirements of RCRA as administered by the Environmental Protection Agency (EPA). The ACS publications, *RCRA and Laboratories* and *The Waste Management Manual for Laboratory Workers,* are recommended. Another excellent source of information is the book, *Hazardous Waste Management at Educational Institutions.* For more detail on the federal regulations, Title 40 of the Code of Federal Regulations (CFR), Parts 260-268 should be consulted. Always obtain detailed and up-to-date information from local environmental agency offices so as to ensure compliance with current local and state regulations as well.

Within the federal regulations, hazardous wastes are those chemical wastes that are included on one of several regulatory lists (listed wastes) or fit the defined characteristics as ignitable, corrosive, reactive, or possessing a toxicity characteristic. In general, it is prudent to consider all waste chemicals to be hazardous wastes unless there are good reasons for considering a material to be non-hazardous.

If hazardous wastes are to be shipped off-site for disposal, the institution will need a generator identification number from the EPA and possibly from the state regulatory agency as well. There is no cost to obtain an identification number. Call the RCRA Hotline (800-424-9346) to obtain the appropriate form.

Most academic institutions work with a reliable disposal contractor. The contractor, who must have the necessary EPA permits and authorizations, performs some or all of the following services:
- packs the wastes properly
- labels the containers properly
- prepares the necessary forms including a manifest
- distributes the forms to the proper destinations
- transports the wastes to the disposal site for disposal
- certifies that the wastes have been properly disposed of

The waste generator (the institution) is still liable for its waste even after handling by the disposal contractor. Therefore, the selection of a competent and reliable contractor is essential. It may be useful to delay payment until a certificate of final disposal is received. In this way, one can ensure that proper disposal was accomplished.

Disposal of hazardous wastes is expensive. However, there are a number of steps that can taken to control costs. The first step is to control quantities purchased. The next step is to develop a clearly defined line of responsibility for chemical waste management. This means that one person is assigned responsibility for coordinating the hazardous waste management program. This person becomes familiar with regulatory requirements, develops internal handling procedures, and works with contractors to arrange for disposal of hazardous wastes as required. Finally, each individual working with chemicals must understand that all containers must have their contents labeled. Analytical costs to identify the contents of unlabeled containers are high and unnecessary if chemists do their job properly.

In any activity where waste chemicals are generated, chemically different substances should be kept separate. When hazardous and non-hazardous wastes are mixed, they are considered to be hazardous waste, thereby increasing the volume of hazardous waste to be disposed of. Additionally, if waste chemicals must be disposed of off-site, more options are available if the various types of waste are kept separate. For a description of compatibility testing in an academic environment, see J. C. Chang, S. P. Levine, and M. S. Simmons in *J. Chem. Ed.* v63(7), July 1986.

Once good tracking procedures have been implemented, other management strategies can be pursued. These strategies include:
- purchasing of minimum quantities
- waste minimization
- recycling and reuse
- treatment or incineration
- disposal in an approved hazardous waste landfill

High disposal costs are associated with the last two options which may also require special permits. Therefore it is in the institution's economic interest, as well as its environmental interest, to pursue the first three options as much as possible. Reduce or eliminate the production of waste chemicals by modifying the laboratory procedure or by using a different method. Disposal problems can be reduced by working with minimal quantities of reagents and using the least quantities to demonstrate the principles of student experiments. For more information, see *Less is Better,* a publication of the American Chemical Society. Examine possibilities for recycling and reuse; *e.g.,* mercury can be shipped for rerefining at low cost. In addition, chemical exchanges between laboratories may be possible. Redistribution of suitable chemicals not only avoids disposal costs, but also creates savings through avoided purchase costs. However, be cautious in accepting donations of old chemicals which may present disposal problems outweighing their value.

If wastes must be shipped off-site for disposal, consider treatment or incineration as more desirable than landfilling. Though often more costly, treatment or incineration will minimize the potential for future liability. In the case of landfills, the waste will be sitting in the ground as a potential accident waiting to happen in even the best designed landfill. Furthermore, the landfill option is being phased out. Soon, virtually all hazardous wastes will be banned from disposal in landfills unless the wastes are pretreated.

One may wish to consider in-house treatment methods to better manage wastes and lower disposal costs. Discussions of waste disposal and waste treatment methods can be found in *Prudent Practices for the Disposal of Hazardous Chemicals from the Laboratory, Procedures for Laboratory Destruction of Chemicals* by B. C. McKusick, and *Hazardous Chemicals Information and Disposal Guide* by M. A. Armour and others. It should be noted that, except for elementary neutralization, all procedures for treating hazardous wastes may require a permit. In the case of laboratories, treatment techniques that are a part of the experimental protocol do not require a permit. Therefore, experiments should be carefully planned so that treatment of hazardous products from experimental work is an integral part of the overall procedure.

Finally, it is important to keep records both of waste chemicals on hand and of those that have been discarded. At a minimum, the name of the person responsible, the chemical identity or description of the waste, the amount, the date designated as a waste, the date of disposal, and the location of the disposal site should be recorded. All such records must be retained for at least three years; however, the institution may wish to keep such records indefinitely.

Waste Classification Terminology

Disposal procedures require an understanding of EPA waste classification terminology. This terminology is quite specific and cannot necessarily be inferred from a general knowledge of chemistry. Specific disposal instructions include the following waste classification and treatment guidelines:

Ignitability: A solid waste exhibits the characteristic of ignitability (40 CFR 261.21) if the waste exists in any of the following forms:
- Liquid, other than an aqueous solution containing less than 24 percent alcohol by volume and with a flash point less than 60° C (140° F).
- Non-liquid, which under standard conditions is capable of causing fire through friction, absorption of moisture, or spontaneous chemical changes, and, when ignited, burns in a manner that creates a hazard
- Ignitable compressed gas (Refer to 49 CFR 173.300 and test methods therein)
- Oxidizer (Refer to 49 CFR 173.151 for definition).

Corrosivity: A solid waste exhibits the characteristic of corrosivity (Refer to 40 CFR 261.11) if the waste is
- Aqueous and has a pH less than or equal to 2, or greater than 12.5, using EPA-specified or approved test methods, or
- Liquid and corrodes steel (SAE 1020) at a rate greater than 6.35 mm (0.250 inch) per year at a test temperature of 55° C (130° F).

Reactivity: A solid waste exhibits the characteristic of reactivity (Refer to 40 CFR 261.23) if the waste
- is normally unstable and readily undergoes violent change without detonation, or

- reacts violently with water, or
- forms potentially explosive mixtures with water, or
- generates toxic gases, vapors, or fumes when mixed with water, or
- is a cyanide or sulfide bearing waste that generates toxic gases, vapors, or fumes at a pH between 2 and 12.5, or
- is capable of detonation or explosive reaction when subject to a strong initiating source or if heated in confinement.

Toxicity Characteristic: A solid waste exhibits this characteristic when EPA defined test procedures indicate that an extract derived from the waste contains at least one of a specified group of heavy metals, organic toxicants and pesticides at a higher level than the regulatory level. The toxicity characteristic only deals with the risk to human health by groundwater contamination and not environmental risks or risks to human health by other methods of exposure. There are 39 chemicals including the heavy metals, barium, lead, mercury and silver, on the list.

OSHA Laboratory Standard

In January 1990, OSHA published the final rule "Occupational Exposures to Hazardous Chemicals in Laboratories". For the academic community, this rule recognizes that the exposure potential for laboratory scale work with hazardous materials may be different than exposures in the industrial sector.

The main component of the OSHA laboratory standard is the requirement for a written Chemical Hygiene Plan (CHP). This CHP can be developed within the specific circumstances of the laboratory operations. This allows considerable flexibility for the laboratory administrator to develop appropriate plans consistent with the OSHA intent of minimizing hazards to workers. The Chemical Hygiene Plan must include the following major elements:
- Standard operating procedures
- Criteria for implementing specific control measures
- A requirement that fume hoods function properly
- Information and training requirements
- Circumstances under which a particular laboratory operation shall require prior approval from the employer
- Provisions for medical consultation and exams
- Designation of a Chemical Hygiene Officer
- Provisions for additional protection for work with select carcinogens, reproductive toxins and substances with a high degree of acute toxicity [1]

The new rule takes effect May 1, 1990, and laboratories must have their Chemical Hygiene Plan in place by January 31, 1991.

---

1 *Summary by J. A. Parr, ACS Department of Government Relations and Science Policy.*

Other OSHA and EPA Requirements

Generally, the OSHA regulations, Title 29 of the Code of Federal Regulations (29 CFR) are applicable to academic institutions. Some of the regulations which are not well known are here identified; the section identification refers to the section, or subpart, of 29 CFR:

(a) The employer's safety and health protection policy must be posted. See section 1903.2(a)(1) and (2). Whether the state or federal posting is required depends upon the existence of a state plan. The requirements for posting in multiple work locations should be carefully reviewed.

(b) A written emergency action plan and a written fire protection plan must be prepared. See sections 1910.38(a) and 1910.38(b).

(c) Portable fire extinguishers must be inspected monthly. See 1910.156(d). Hands-on training in the use of fire extinguishers must be provided annually. See 1910.157(g).

(d) Safety shower and eye wash facilities must meet the requirements of section 1910.151(c) and be tested monthly. Also see ANSI Z358.1 - 1981 or current standard.

(e) Respirators must be inspected and records maintained. See section 1910.134.

The requirements of the Hazard Communication Standard were extended to employers outside of the manufacturing sector in 1988. This standard is found in 29 CFR part 1910.1200.

The EPA requires that a contingency plan including spill prevention, control and countermeasures for fires, explosion or accidental releases, and hazardous waste management be prepared. Details are given in 40 CFR part 265.50 - 265.56, and 265.112.

It is highly recommended that copies of 29 CFR and 40 CFR be obtained and thoroughly studied. These publications are updated daily by the *Federal Register* and are revised annually. They can be obtained from the Superintendent of Documents, US Government Printing Office, Washington, DC 20402. Further information can be obtained from the Regional EPA and OSHA offices.

A number of states have regulations which require written plans or other reports. Check with the appropriate state authorities or agencies for information.

Peroxides

Peroxy compounds are examples of chemicals which present special problems in the laboratory because they can be violently reactive or explosive. Their handling deserves careful attention.

Inorganic Peroxides

Inorganic peroxy compounds are generally stable as such, but in contact with organic compounds may generate organic peroxides and hydroperoxides. Their contact with any combustible material may lead to a fire or explosion. They must be stored, handled and used with much caution. Peroxides of alkali metals are not sensitive to shock, but are decomposed slowly by moisture and violently by bulk water. The most common inorganic peroxy compounds are sodium peroxide, hydrogen peroxide, sodium perborate, and sodium persulfate. The high weight alkali metals readily form superoxides, and ozonides such as KO_3 are known.

Any of these peroxy compounds can pose a threat of fire or explosion when contacted by oxidizable materials. They can react violently with water and many other substances. Small spills can be treated cautiously with water and sodium bisulfite solution; larger ones should be taken up with inert solids such as vermiculite, sand or salt and treated with bisulfite in a safe area. Any person burned by these chemicals should be washed gently but thoroughly and given competent medical attention.

Organic Peroxides and Hydroperoxides

Organic peroxy compounds fall largely into four classes: dialkyl or diarylalkyl peroxides, peracids, diacyl peroxides, and alkyl or arylalkyl hydroperoxides. All are unstable to some degree and generally are not offered in high purity for their hazards increase with concentration. The hazard decreases with increasing molecular weight because of the dilution effect. Those of lower molecular weight can deflagrate or detonate. Some of the most common ones are tert-butyl peroxide, tert-butyl hydroperoxide, peracetic acid, benzoyl peroxide and iso-propylbenzene (cumene) hydroperoxide.

Because peroxy compounds are unstable and decompose continuously, bulk quantities may generate enough heat to autoaccelerate up to ignition or explosion. They are sensitive to heat, friction, impact and light as well as to strong oxidizing and reducing agents. All organic peroxides are quite flammable and fires involving bulk quantities should be approached with extreme caution. Because they can generate free radicals with catalytic power, their presence as a contaminant in a reaction mixture can change the course of a planned reaction.

Organic peroxy compounds are generally more stable when water is present. For example, benzoyl peroxide is a solid (m.p. 104-106 dec.) which can ignite or explode from heat, impact or friction, and which must be kept moist in storage. The unscrewing of a lid covered with the dry chemical can set off the entire lot. No more than a short term supply should be kept on hand and the container must be checked at regular intervals. If in doubt, it is best to call an expert on disposal of dangerous chemicals.

Peroxide Formers and Their Storage and Handling

Peroxide formers react with oxygen even at low concentrations and ordinary temperatures to form peroxy compounds which are usually hydroperoxides. In addition to any other hazards that they have, they pose a "peroxide threat" especially if the oxygenated product crystallizes out or becomes concentrated by evaporation or distillation of the unoxidized part. Peroxide crystals may even form at the threads of a sealing plug or cap.

There are four main groups of compounds known to be peroxide precursors:

- Ethers with primary and/or secondary alkyl groups, including open chain and cyclic ethers, acetals and ketals
- Hydrocarbons with allylic, benzylic or propargylic hydrogens
- Conjugated dienes, eneynes and diynes
- Saturated hydrocarbons with exposed tertiary hydrogens

Some specific and typical examples are diethyl ether, di-isopropyl ether, tetrahydrofuran (THF), p-dioxane, cyclohexane, isopropylbenzene (cumene), tetrahydronaphthalene (tetralin), divinylacetylene, decahydronaphthalene and 2,5-dimethylhexane.

Peroxidation is generally a problem of the liquid state. Solid peroxide formers present little problem except when finely divided, for the reaction, if any, will occur only at the surface. Peroxidation seems to be no problem within gases and vapors. For liquids, the peroxidation typically occurs when containers are not fully sealed and blanketed with inert gas. Breathing then occurs with changes in temperature and barometric pressure and oxygen gets into the containers. Peroxide buildup is usually slow because the exchange of atmosphere containing only twenty percent oxygen is usually slow.

If abundant oxygen is supplied to a fast peroxide former, typically there is an induction period, then a relatively fast accumulation of hydroperoxide which tapers off at a maximum level, perhaps 5-15%. Then, the concentration will stabilize or even decrease because the hydroperoxide itself undergoes decomposition and forms byproducts such as alcohols and water which interfere with the free radical chain reaction or peroxidation. The byproduct content may continue to grow, but the peroxide content does not. CAUTION: This scenario does not apply when peroxides separate in solid form. Then the peroxy substance is undiluted by solvent or byproducts and is an immediate threat.

Peroxide formers cannot form peroxy compounds without exposure to oxygen or oxidizers. Therefore their containers should always be tightly sealed. Air should always be flushed out of the free space with an inert gas (usually nitrogen) before sealing. Plastic caps, stoppers and plugs should be used to reduce corrosion and friction.

Precautions for storing and handling peroxide formers are summarized here:

(a) Label the chemicals as known peroxide formers or (in some cases) as possible peroxide formers.

(b) Limit the stock of any item to three months supply or less, and discard remaining stock unless found to be essentially peroxide free.

(c) Always maintain an inert atmosphere (nitrogen or argon) in the free space of each container. Either flush with a stream of the gas, or use pressure siphoning with the gas when withdrawals are made.

(d) Unless it would compromise the material's usefulness, add an oxidation inhibitor to it. The recommended amount is from 0.001 to 0.01% of inhibitors such as hydroquinone, 4-tert-butylcatechol (TBC) or 2,6-di-tert-butyl-p-methylphenol (BHT).

(e) Before distilling any known or suspected peroxide former, check it carefully for peroxide. If any is present, eliminate it by chemical treatment or percolation, or add an inert high boiling substance (such as mineral oil) to prevent the peroxide from concentrating to a dangerous level.

A variety of chemicals used as solvents or in synthesis, even alcohols, have been found to contain significant amounts of peroxides (as high as 0.1 percent). Such small amounts could arise from impurities which are peroxide formers. However, a severe laboratory explosion in the distillation of 2-propanol has been attributed to peroxide content. Pending further investigation, prudence suggests that all oxidizable organic liquids should be checked for peroxides before distillation or use in reactions sensitive to peroxide catalysis.

Detection and Determination of Peroxides

The presence of most peroxy compounds, including all hydroperoxides, can be detected by this test: Mix 1-3 mL of the liquid to be tested and an equal volume of acetic acid in a test tube, add a few drops of five percent potassium iodide solution, and shake. The appearance of a yellow-to-brown color indicates presence of a peroxide. If the color is faint, run a blank to make sure the test is really positive. A semi-quantitative testing kit using treated paper strips is available. Quantitative titration procedures are available.

Disposal of Peroxides

CAUTION: Only a "bomb squad" should dispose of pure peroxides. Peroxides normally must be diluted before disposal.

Small quantities (25 g or less) of peroxides are generally disposed of by diluting with water to a concentration of 2% or less and then transferring them to a polyethylene disposal bottle containing an aqueous solution of a reducing agent such as ferrous sulfate or sodium bisulfite. The material is then handled like any other waste chemical, but it must not be mixed with other chemicals for disposal. Spilled peroxides should be absorbed on vermiculite as quickly as possible. The vermiculite-peroxide mixture may then be burned directly or may be stirred with a suitable solvent to form a slurry, which is then treated as above. CAUTION: Never flush organic peroxides down the drain.

Large quantities (more than 25 g) of peroxide require special handling. Each case should be considered separately and a handling, storage and disposal procedure, determined by the physical and chemical properties of the particular peroxide and prevailing regulations, established. In preparing a disposal procedure, consult "Destroying Peroxides of Isopropyl Ether," by A. C. Hamstead, *Ind. Eng. Chem., 1964*, 56(6), 37.

Thioacetamide

Thioacetamide is commonly used as a source of hydrogen sulfide. Hydrogen sulfide smells like rotten eggs and is so offensive that it can be detected in minute concentrations. However, upon continued exposure, the olfactory nerve seems to become paralyzed and then an increase in concentration of the chemical is not noticed by the victim, leading to death by hydrogen sulfide poisoning. Thioacetamide poses the additional hazard of being an anticipated carcinogen. Several sources listed in Appendix II discuss thioacetamide use and precautions.

Appendices

Appendix I

Properties of Protective Clothing Materials*

For the most current information in this area, consult the National Institute for Occupational Safety and Health (NIOSH) protective equipment program.

Material	Strength	Properties Chemical Resistance	Flammability	Static Properties	Comfort	Uses
Cotton	Fair durability	Degraded by acids, binds	Special treatment for flame	No static problems	Comfortable lightweight	Lab Coats
Modacrylic	Resistant to rips & tears, but less so than polyamide fibers. Abrasion resistant but less so than nylon or polyester	Resistant to most chemicals	In direct flame fabric shrinks to resist flame penetration. Will not melt or drip. Self extinguishing. Rapidly dissipates when source of ignition is removed.	Has antistatic properties	Comfortable, soft & resilient. Easy to clean & has soil release properties	Lab Coats
Nylon	Exceptionally strong & abrasion resistant	Not water absorbent	Melts when heated; requires flame retardant	Static buildup possible Requires antistatic agent	Lightweight	Lab Coats
Plastic	Usually reinforced at points of strain, will not stick together, peel, crack, or stiffen	Resistant to corrosive chemicals.	Can be ignited by flammable solvents & others in event of static discharge	Accumulates considerable charge of static electricity	Lightweight	Aprons, Sleeve Protectors, Boots
Polyolefin	Resistant to rips & tears	Excellent chemical resistance. Low binding for chemicals	High melting point Flame resistant	Good static dissociation	Lightweight. Good permeability. Limited moisture absorbence May be uncomfortable if perspiring.	Bouffant Caps
Polypropylene	Strong	Resistant to most chemicals, oxygen & light sensitive	Low melting point; requires flame retardant	Static buildup requires anti-static agent	Lightweight	Aprons
Rayon	Fairly durable	Degraded by acids, binds some chemicals.				Lab Coats

*Based on manufacturers' claims

Appendix II

Sources of Additional Information

Books and Journal Articles

All books, even the best ones, may become outdated after they are published. Readers must make continual efforts to update their knowledge in the quickly changing field of chemical safety. To assist readers, the titles in the following bibliography that are regularly updated are marked by an asterisk.

"Adult CPR"; American Red Cross: Washington, DC, 1987.

* "Annual Report on Carcinogens"; DHHS (NTP), 5th ed.; Summary from National Toxicology Program, Public Information Office: Research Triangle Park, NC, 1989.

Ammore, J. E. and Hautala, E. "Odor as an Aid to Chemical Safety: Odor Thresholds Compared with Threshold Limit Values and Volatilities for 214 Industrial Chemicals in Air and Water Dilution" *J. Appl. Toxicol.* 1983, 3(6), 272.

Armour, M. A.; Browne, L. M.; Weir, G. L. "Hazardous Chemicals: Information and Disposal Guide"; Department of Chemistry, University of Alberta: Edmonton, Alberta, 1982.

* *Best's Safety Directory*; A. M. Best: Oldwick, NY (revised annually).

Beyler, R. E.; Myers, V. K. "What Every Chemist Should Know About Teratogens" *J. Chem. Ed.* 1982, 59, 759.

Braker, W.; Mossman, A. L. *Effects of Exposure to Toxic Gases: First Aid and Medical Treatment*, 2nd ed.; Matheson Gas Products: East Rutherford, NJ, 1977.

Braker, W.; Mossman, A. L. *Gas Data Book*, 6th ed.; Matheson Gas Products: East Rutherford, NJ, 1981.

Bretherick, L. *Handbook of Reactive Chemicals Hazards*, 3rd ed.; Butterworths: London, 1985.

Bretherick, L. *Hazards in the Chemical Laboratory*, 4th ed.; Royal Society of Chemistry: London, 1986.

Carcinogens—Regulation and Control: A Management Guide to Carcinogens, Regulation and Control; NIOSH, DHEW Publication No. 77-205; Government Printing Office: Washington, DC, 1977.

Carcinogens—Working with Carcinogens—Regulation and Control: Working with Carcinogens: A Guide to Good Health Practices; NIOSH, DHEW Publication No. 77-206; Government Printing Office, Washington, DC, 1977.

Chang, J. C.; Levine, S. P.; and Simmons, M. S. "A Laboratory Exercise for Compatibility Testing of Hazardous Wastes in an Environmental Analysis Course" *J. Chem. Ed.* 1986, 63, 640.

Chemical and Engineering News [Letters to the Editor]; American Chemical Society: Washington, DC.

"Chemical Hazard Communication"; OSHA Publication No. 3084; Occupational Safety and Health Administration: Washington, DC, 1987.

* *Chemical Guide to the OSHA Hazard Communication Standard*; Clansky, R. B., Ed.; Roytech: Burlingame, CA (revised annually).

"Chemical Risk: Personal Decisions"; Department of Government Relations and Science Policy, American Chemical Society: Washington, DC, 1990.

Clinical Toxicology of Commercial Products, Acute Poisoning, 5th ed.; Goselin,

R. E., Ed.; Williams and Wilkins: Baltimore, 1984.

"Design of Safe Chemical Laboratories: Suggested References" [pamphlet]; Committee on Chemical Safety, American Chemical Society: Washington, DC, 1988.

DiBerardinis, L. J., et al; *Guidelines for Laboratory Design: Health and Safety Considerations*; Wiley-Interscience: New York, 1987.

Dreisbach, R. H.; Robertson, *W. O. Handbook of Poisoning: Diagnosis and Treatment*, 12th ed.; Appleton and Lange: Los Altos, CA, 1987.

* "Emergency Eyewash and Shower Equipment"; ANSI Standard Z358.1-1981; American National Standards Institute: New York, 1981.

"Evaluation of Organic Peroxides from Half-Life Data"; Technical Bulletin; Wallace and Tiernan, Lucidol Division: Buffalo, NY, 1964.

Fawcett, H. H. *Hazardous and Toxic Materials: Safe Handling and Disposal*, 2nd ed.; Wiley/Interscience: New York, 1988.

"Fire and Explosion Hazards of Peroxy Compounds"; ASTM Special Technical Publication 394; American Society for Testing and Materials: Philadelphia, 1965.

* "Fire Protection for Laboratories Using Chemicals"; NFPA Standard 45; National Fire Protection Association: Quincy, MA, 1987.

* "Fire Protection Guide on Hazardous Materials" [contains NFPA 325M, NFPA 49, NFPA 491M, and NFPA 704]; National Fire Protection Association: Quincy, MA, (current edition).

* "Flammable and Combustible Liquids Code"; NFPA Standard 30; National Fire Protection Association: Quincy, MA, 1987.

"Forum on Hazardous Waste Management at Academic Institutions"; Department of Public Affairs, American Chemical Society, Washington, DC, 1980.

* "Fume Hoods, Methods of Testing Performance of Laboratory; ANSI/ASHRAE Standard 110-1985; American Society of Heating, Refrigerating, and Air Conditioning Engineers: Atlanta, GA, 1985.

Fuscaldo, A. A.; Erlick, B. J.; Hindman, B. *Laboratory Safety: Theory and Practice*; Academic: New York, 1980.

Hamstead, A. C. "Destroying Peroxides of Isopropyl Ether" *Ind. Eng. Chem. 1964*, 56(6), 37.

Handbook of Compressed Gases, 2nd ed.; Compressed Gas Association: New York, 1981.

Hazard Classification Systems: Comparative Guide to Definitions and Labels; Hazardous Materials Information Center; Inter/Face: Middletown, CT, 1986.

* "Hazardous Industrial Chemicals—Precautionary Labeling"; ANSI Standard Z129.1-1988; American National Standards Institute: New York, 1988.

Hazardous Waste Management at Educational Institutions; National Association of University Business Officers: Washington, DC, 1987.

* "Hazardous Waste Management Facilities in the United States"; EPA Publication No. 8W-146-3; Environmental Protection Agency: Cincinnati, OH (revised annually).

* *IARC Monographs on the Evaluation of Carcinogenic Risk of Chemicals to Humans*; International Agency for Research on Cancer: Lyon, France.

"Industrial Exposure and Control Technologies for OSHA Regulated Hazardous Substances"; Department of Labor: Washington, DC, 1989.

* *Industrial Ventilation*; American Conference of Governmental and Industrial Hygienists: Cincinnati, OH, 1986.

Improving Safety in the Chemical Laboratory: A Practical Guide; Young, J. A. Ed.; Wiley/Interscience: New York, 1987.

Information Resources in Toxicology; Wexler, P., Ed.; Elsevier: New York, 1981.

Journal of Chemical Education [Safety in the Chemical Laboratory column];
   Division of Chemical Education: Easton, PA.
Kletz, T. *Learning from Accidents in Industry*; Butterworths: London, 1988.
"Less is Better—Laboratory Chemical Management for Waste Reduction";
   Department of Government Relations and Science Policy, American
   Chemical Society: Washington, DC, 1985.
Mageli, O. L.; Noller, D. C.; Mazurowski, S. J.; Linden; G. F.; De Leeuw,
   F. J. F. "A Relative Hazard Classification of Commercial Peroxides";
   Reprint 30.42; Wallace and Tiernan, Lucidol Division: Buffalo, NY.
   Published in part, *Ind. Eng. Chem.* 56, 18-27 (1964).
* "Manual of Hazardous Chemical Reactions"; NFPA Manual 491M;
   National Fire Protection Association: Quincy, MA, 1986.
Mayo, D. D. W.; *et al. Microscale Organic Laboratory*; Wiley: New York, 1989.
McKusick, B. C. "Procedures for Laboratory Destruction of Chemicals"
   J. Chem. Ed. 1984, 61, A152.
* *The Merck Index: An Encyclopedia of Chemicals, Drugs, and Biologicals*,
   11th ed.; Merck: Rahway, NJ, 1989.
Meyer, E. *Chemistry of Hazardous Materials*; Prentice-Hall: Englewood
   Cliffs, NJ, 1977.
Mikell, W. G.; Drinkard, W. C. "Good Practices for Hood Use" *J. Chem. Ed.*
   1984, 61, A13.
Mikell, W. G.; Fuller, F. H. "Good Hood Practices for Safe Hood Operation"
   J. Chem. Ed. 1988, 65, A36.
Mikell, W. G.; Hobbs, L. R. "Laboratory Hood Studies" *J. Chem. Ed.*
   1981, 58, A165.
* *National Electrical Code*; Vol. 5 of the National Fire Codes, National
   Fire Protection Association: Quincy, MA (revised annually).
NIH Guidelines for the Laboratory Use of Chemical Carcinogens; NIH, DHSS;
   Government Printing Office: Washington, DC, 1981.
"NIOSH/OSHA Pocket Guide to Chemical Hazards"; Mackison, F. W.;
   Stricoff, R. S.; Partridge, L. J.; Eds.; DHHS (NIOSH); Government
   Printing Office: Washington, DC, 1987.
Occupational Health Guidelines for Chemical Hazards; 3 vols; DHHS (NIOSH)
   Publication No. 81-123; Government Printing Office: Washington,
   DC, 1981.
Patty's Industrial Hygiene and Toxicology; Clayton, G. D.; Clayton, F. E., Eds.;
   6 pts. 3rd ed.; Wiley/Interscience: New York, 1985.
Phifer, R. W.; McTigue, W. R., Jr. *Handbook of Hazardous Waste
   Management for Small Quantity Generators*; Lewis: Chelsea, MI, 1988.
Pitt, M. J.; Pitt, E. *Handbook of Laboratory Waste Disposal: A Practical
   Manual*; Halsted: New York, 1985.
Pitt, M. J. "Please Do Not Touch—Some Thoughts on Temporary Labels in
   the Laboratory"; *J. Chem. Ed.* 1984, 61, A231.
* "Practice for Occupational and Educational Eye and Face Protection";
   ANSI Standard Z87.1-1989; American National Standards Institute:
   New York, 1989.
* "Practices for Respiratory Protection"; ANSI Standard Z88.2-1980;
   American National Standards Institute: New York, 1980.
"Proposed Guide for Estimating the Incompatibility of Selected
   Hazardous Wastes Based on Binary Chemical Reactions"; ASTM P168;
   ASTM: Philadelphia, 1986.
Prudent Practices for Handling Hazardous Chemicals in Laboratories;
   National Academy of Sciences: Washington, DC, 1981.
*Prudent Practices for the Disposal of Hazardous Chemicals from the
   Laboratory*; National Academy of Sciences: Washington, DC, 1983.
"RCRA and Laboratories"; Department of Government Relations and

Science Policy, American Chemical Society: Washington, DC, 1986.
* "Registry of Toxic Effects of Chemical Substances"; DHHS (NIOSH); Government Printing Office: Washington, DC, [Available in print with microfiche updates or online from the Toxicology Information Program of the National Library of Medicine].

Reproductive Health Hazards in the Workplace; Office of Technology Assessment; Government Printing Office: Washington, DC, 1985.

Safe Handling of Chemical Carcinogens, Mutagens, Teratogens, and Highly Toxic Substances; Walters, D. B., Ed.; Ann Arbor Science: Ann Arbor, MI, 1980.

Safety and Accident Prevention in Chemical Operations; Fawcett, H. H.; Wood, W. S., Eds.; Wiley: New York, 1982.

"Safety in the Chemical Laboratory", 4 vols.; Reprints from *J. Chem. Ed.* Journal of Chemical Education: Easton, PA, 1964-1980.

Safe Storage of Laboratory Chemicals; Pipitone, D.A., Ed.; Wiley/Interscience: New York, 1984.

Saunders, G.T. "Updating Older Fume Hoods" *J. Chem. Ed.* 1985, 62, A178.

Saunders, G.T. "Upgrading Laboratory Fume Hoods" *J. Chem. Ed.* 1987, 64, A272.

Shepard, T. H. *Catalog of Teratogenic Agents*, 6th ed.; Johns Hopkins: Baltimore, 1989.

Sittig, M. *Handbook of Toxic and Hazardous Chemicals and Carcinogens*, 2nd ed.; Noyes: Park Ridge, NJ, 1985.

"Standard First Aid and Personal Safety", 3rd ed.; American Red Cross: Washington, DC, 1987.

"Standard for Hazard Communication"; 29 CFR 1910.1200; 48 FR 53340-48 (November 25, 1983).

"Standard for Occupational Exposures to Hazardous Chemicals in Laboratories"; 29 CFR 1910.1450; 55 FR 3327-35 (January 31, 1990).

* "Standard Test Methods for Chemical Permeability"; ASTM Standard F-739; ASTM: Philadelphia, 1988.

* *Suspect Chemicals Sourcebook: Guide to Industrial Chemicals Covered Under Major Federal Regulatory and Advisory Programs*; Clansky, K. B., Ed.; Roytech: Burlingame, CA (revised annually).

* *Threshold Limit Values for Chemical Substances and Physical Agents in the Workroom Environment with Intended Changes*; American Conference of Governmental Industrial Hygienists: Cincinnati, OH (revised annually).

"The Waste Management Manual for Laboratory Workers"; Department of Government Relations and Science Policy, American Chemical Society: Washington, DC, 1990.

Non-Print (Electronic) Media

Chemical toxicity and some regulatory and emergency response information can be often handled in electronic files. Until recently, these files have been almost exclusively available as online databases to which access is measured and sold by connect hour by database vendors. Users need computer terminals and modems as well as vendor assigned passwords to access these databases. Attendance at a user training workshop offered by the database vendor and the willingness to maintain the appropriate documentation are also recommended. As an alternative, almost all academic libraries offer database search services. Finally, the database vendors themselves will perform searches for customers.

The following list of databases is representative of the information that is being offered through online vendors.

OCCUPATIONAL SAFETY AND HEALTH (NIOSH). A bibliographic

database produced by the National Institute for Occupational Safety and Health and available from Dialog® Information Services. It indexes over 150 journals in health and safety and covers all NIOSH publications.

CHEMLIST (formerly TOXLIST, Toxic Regulatory Listings). This database has information on materials in the TSCA (Toxic Substances Control Act) inventory. It covers regulatory activities such as premanufacture notices and EPA rule making. It is produced by the American Petroleum Institute and available from STN International.

The TOXICOLOGY INFORMATION PROGRAM from the National Library of Medicine offers these relevant databases:
   (a) RTECS (REGISTRY OF TOXIC EFFECTS OF CHEMICAL SUBSTANCES) is a factual database giving acute and chronic toxicity information for more than 84,000 chemicals. It is also available in paper/microfiche.
   (b) TOXLINE is a bibliographic database covering the toxicological and physiological effects of drugs and other chemicals.
   (c) HSDB (HAZARDOUS SUBSTANCES DATA BANK) contains reviewed data on environmental and regulatory issues as well as toxicological information for over 4000 chemicals.

CD-ROM Products

Several of the databases listed above as well as many others are also available as CD-ROM (compact disk read only memory) products. In the most commonly available format, the disks store approximately 550 megabytes of information. The services are usually sold by subscription with at least quarterly updates. To use the CD-ROM disks, a personal computer with a monitor and (optional) printer and a CD-ROM player are needed. CD-ROM products should be considered when there is potentially high use of online files or when the files themselves (such as collections of MSDSs) are well-adapted to the format. The number of databases which are commercially available on CD-ROM is growing rapidly.

Three representative products are listed below:
   (a) CHEM-BANK which is available from SilverPlatter. This disk has the RTECS file, the OHMTADS (Oil and Hazardous Materials Technical Assistance Data Systems) file from the EPA, and the CHRIS (Chemical Hazards Response Information System) from the U. S. Coast Guard.
   (b) OHS MSDS ON DISK is a database containing the material safety data sheets of 9,000 commonly used chemicals. Occupational Health Services also allows subscribers access to the 70,000 material safety data sheets which are contained in its online database.
   (c) CCINFOdisc which is produced by the Canadian Centre for Occupational Health and Safety contains the following files: TRADE NAMES with 56,000 MSDSs, the RTECS file, CHEMINFO with health and safety information on chemicals from industrial processes, and several bibliographic health and safety files.

Appendix III
Incompatible Chemicals

The following list is to be used only as a guide. Specific incompatibilities are listed in the material safety data sheets. One may also wish to consult Bretherick's "Handbook of Reactive Chemical Hazards".

Chemical	Incompatible With
Acetic acid	Chromic acid, nitric acid, hydroxyl compounds, ethylene glycol, perchloric acid, peroxides, permanganates
Acetylene	Chlorine, bromine, copper, fluorine, silver, mercury
Acetone	Concentrated nitric and sulfuric acid mixtures
Alkali and alkaline earth metals (such as powdered aluminum or magnesium calcium, lithium, sodium, potassium)	Water, carbon tetrachloride or other chlorinated hydrocarbons, carbon dioxide, halogens
Ammonia (anhydrous)	Mercury (e.g., in manometers), chlorine, calcium hypochlorite, iodine, bromine, hydrofluoric acid (anhydrous)
Ammonium nitrate	Acids, powdered metals, flammable liquids, chlorates, nitrites, sulfur, finely divided organic combustible materials
Aniline	Nitric acid, hydrogen peroxide
Arsenical materials	Any reducing agent
Azides	Acids
Bromine	See chlorine
Calcium oxide	Water
Carbon (activated)	Calcium hypochlorite, all oxidizing agents
Chlorates	Ammonium salts, acids, powdered metals, sulfur, finely divided organic or combustible materials
Chromic acid and chromium trioxide	Acetic acid, naphthalene, camphor, glycerol, alcohol, flammable liquids in general
Chlorine	Ammonia, acetylene, butadiene, butane, methane, propane (or other petroleum gases), hydrogen, sodium carbide, benzene, finely divided metals, turpentine
Chlorine dioxide	Ammonia, methane, phosphine, hydrogen sulfide
Copper	Acetylene, hydrogen peroxide
Cumene hydroperoxide	Acids (organic or inorganic)
Cyanides	Acids
Flammable liquids	Ammonium nitrate, chromic acid, hydrogen peroxide, nitric acid, sodium peroxide, halogens

Fluorine	All other chemicals
Hydrocarbons (such as butane, propane, benzene)	Fluorine, chlorine, bromine, chromic acid, sodium peroxide
Hydrocyanic acid	Nitric acid, alkali
Hydrofluoric acid (anhydrous)	Ammonia (aqueous or anhydrous)
Hydrogen sulfide	Fuming nitric acid, oxidizing gases
Hypochlorites	Acids, activated carbon
Iodine	Acetylene, ammonia (aqueous or anhydrous), hydrogen
Mercury	Acetylene, fulminic acid, ammonia
Nitrates	Acids
Nitric acid (concentrated)	Acetic acid, aniline, chromic acid, hydrocyanic acid, hydrogen sulfide, flammable liquids and gases, copper, brass, any heavy metals
Nitrites	Acids
Nitroparaffins	Inorganic bases, amines
Oxalic acid	Silver, mercury
Oxygen	Oils, grease, hydrogen; flammable liquids, solids, and gases
Perchloric acid	Acetic anhydride, bismuth and its alloys, alcohol, paper, wood, grease, oils
Peroxides, organic	Acids (organic or mineral), avoid friction, store cold
Phosphorus (white)	Air, oxygen, alkalies, reducing agents
Potassium	Carbon tetrachloride, carbon dioxide, water
Potassium chlorate	Sulfuric and other acids
Potassium perchlorate see also chlorates	Sulfuric and other acids
Potassium permanganate	Glycerol, ethylene glycol, benzaldehyde, sulfuric acid
Selenides	Reducing agents
Silver	Acetylene, oxalic acid, tartaric acid, ammonium compounds, fulminic acid
Sodium	Carbon tetrachloride, carbon dioxide, water
Sodium nitrite	Ammonium nitrate and other ammonium salts
Sodium peroxide	Ethyl or methyl alcohol, glacial acetic acid, acetic anhydride, benzaldehyde, carbon disulfide, glycerin, ethylene glycol, ethylacetate, methyl acetate, furfural
Sulfides	Acids
Sulfuric acid	Potassium chlorate, potassium perchlorate, potassium permanganate (similar compounds of light metals, such as sodium, lithium)
Tellurides	Reducing agents

Appendix IV

Maximum Allowable Container Capacity[1]

Container Type	Flammable Liquids[2]			Combustible Liquids[2]	
	IA	IB	IC	I	IIIA
Glass	1 pt[3]	1 qt[3]	1 gal	1 gal	5 gal
Metal (other than DOT Drums) or Approved Plastic	1 gal	5 gal[1]	5 gal[4]	5 gal[4]	5 gal
Safety Cans	2 gal	5 gal[4]	5 gal[4]	5 gal[4]	5 gal
Metal Drums (DOT)	N/A[5]	5 gal[4]	5 gal[4]	60 gal[4]	60 gal

1 This table is taken from NFPA 30, *Flammable and Combustible Liquids Code* except for allowable quantities of flammable liquids in metal DOT drums.

2 See B-1 for definitions of the various classes of flammable and combustible liquids.

3 See Exception No. 1 of 7-2.3.2 and A-7-2.3.2.

4 In instructional laboratory work areas, no container for Class I or II liquids shall exceed a capacity of 1 gallon, except that safety cans may be of 2 gallon capacity.

5 N/A = Not allowed. See Exception No. 2 of 7-2.3.2. For SI Units: 1 gal = 3.785 liters; 1 qt = 0.95 liter; 1 pt = 0.48 liter.

Appendix V
Organizations

American Chemical Society, 1155 16th St., N.W., Washington, DC 20036; Abstracts of symposia sponsored or cosponsored by the Council Committee on Chemical Safety since 1963 and the ACS Division of Chemical Health and Safety since 1977. The latter also publishes *CHAS Notes*, a quarterly newsletter and reprint journal. Published Division symposia include:

Toxic Chemical and Explosive Facilities; Scott, R. A., Jr. Ed.; ACS Symposium Series; 96: Washington, 1979.

Analytical Techniques in Occupational Health Chemistry; Dollberg, D. D.; Verstuyft, A. W. Eds.; ACS Symposium Series; 120: Washington, 1980.

Safe Handling of Chemical Carcinogens, Mutagens, Teratogens and Highly Toxic Substances; Walters, D. B., Ed.; Ann Arbor Science: Ann Arbor, MI, 1980.

Chemical Hazards in the Workplace: Measurement and Control; Choudhary, G., Ed.; ACS Symposium Series; 149: Washington, 1981.

Safe Storage of Laboratory Chemicals; Pipitone, D. A., Ed.; Wiley/Interscience: New York, 1984.

Assessment and Management of Chemical Risks; Rodricks, J. V.; Tardiff, R. G. Eds.; ACS Symposium Series; 239: Washington, 1984.

Chemical Process Hazard Review; Hoffmann, J. M.; Maser, D. C. Eds.; ACS Symposium Series; 274: Washington, 1985.

Biological Monitoring of Exposure to Chemicals; Ho, M. H.; Dillion, H. K. Eds.; Wiley: New York, 1987.

Design Considerations for Toxic Chemical and Explosives Facilities; Scott, R. A. Jr.; Doemeny, L. J. Eds.; ACS Symposium Series; 345: Washington, 1987.

American Chemical Society. Washington, DC; Audio course on *Laboratory Safety and Health*, Media Courses Department.

American Conference of Governmental Industrial Hygienists, Bldg. D7, 6500 Glenway Ave., Cincinnati, OH 45211.

American National Standards Institute, 1430 Broadway, New York, NY 10018.

American Society of Heating, Refrigerating and Air Conditioning Engineers, 1791 Tullie Circle, N.E., Atlanta, GA 30329.

ASTM (formerly American Society for Testing and Materials), 1916 Race St., Philadelphia, PA 19103.

Government Printing Office, Superintendent of Documents, Washington, DC 20402.

National Audiovisual Center, 8700 Edgeworth Drive, Capitol Heights, MD 20743. (Mailing Address: Eighth St. and Pennsylvania Ave., N.W., Washington, DC 20409).

National Fire Protection Association, Batterymarch Park, Quincy, MA 02269; *National Fire Codes* (including the *National Electrical Code*), training materials.

National Safety Council, 444 N. Michigan Ave., Chicago, IL 60611; *Accident Facts* (published annually); *Directory of Films and Visual Aids* (chemical section). Bimonthly newsletter (chemical section and research and development section).

National Society to Prevent Blindness, 500 E. Remington Rd., Schaumberg, IL 60173; (films and publications).

National Toxicology Program, Department of Health and Human Services, P.O. Box 12233, Research Triangle Park, NC 27704.

Royal Society of Chemistry, The University, Nottingham, NG7 2RD England, UK; *Laboratory Hazards Bulletin*.

Appendix VI
Regional Offices of U.S. Government Agencies

Table I

Department of Labor
Occupational Safety and Health Administration
Regional Offices

Region I
(CT,* MA, ME, NH, RI, VT*)
16-18 North Street
1 Dock Square Building - 4th Flr.
Boston, MA 02109
Telephone: (617) 223-6710

Region II
(NJ, NY,* Puerto Rico,* Virg.Is.)
201 Varick Street, 6th Floor
New York, NY 10014
Telephone: (212) 337-2378

Region III
(DC, MD,* PA, VA,* WV)
Gateway Building, Suite 2100
3535 Market Street
Philadelphia, PA 19104
Telephone: (215) 596-1201

Region IV
(AL, FL, GA, KY,* MS, NC,*
SC,* TN*)
1375 Peachtree Street, NE
Suite 587
Atlanta, GA 30367
Telephone: (404) 347-3573

Region V
(IL, IN,* MI,* MN,* OH, WI)
230 South Dearborn Street
32nd Floor, Room 3244
Chicago, IL 60604
Telephone: (312) 353-2220

Region VI
(AR, LA, NM,* OK, TX)
525 Griffin Square Building
Room 602
Dallas, TX 75202
Telephone: (214) 767-4731

Region VII
(IA,* KS, MO, NE)
911 Walnut Street, Room 406
Kansas City, MO 64106
Telephone: (816) 374-5861

Region VIII
(CO, MT, ND, SD, UT,* WY*)
Federal Building, Room 1554
1961 Stout Street
Denver, CO 80294
Telephone: (303) 844-3061

Region IX
(American Samoa, AZ,* CA,*
Guam, HI,* NV,* Pacific Tr.Terr.)
P.O. Box 36017
450 Golden Gate Avenue
San Francisco, CA 94102
Telephone: (415) 556-7260

Region X
(AK,* ID, OR,* WA*)
Federal Office Building
909 First Ave., Room 6003
Seattle, WA 98174
Telephone: (206) 422-5930

* These states and territories operate their own OSHA-approved job safety
and health programs (except Connecticut and New York whose plans cover
public employees only).

(From "Chemical Hazard Communication", OSHA 3084, 1987)

Table II

**Environmental Protection Agency
Regional Offices**

Region I
(CT, MA, ME, NH, RI, VT)
John F. Kennedy Federal Building
Room 2203
Boston, MA 02203
Telephone: (617) 565-3715

Region II
(NJ, NY, Puerto Rico, Virg.Is.)
26 Federal Plaza
New York, NY 10278
Telephone: (212) 264-2525

Region III
(DC, MD, PA, VA, WV)
841 Chestnut Street
Philadelphia, PA 19107
Telephone: (215) 597-9800

Region IV
(AL, FL, GA, KY, MS, NC,
SC, TN)
345 Courtland Street, N.E.
Atlanta, GA 30365
Telephone: (404) 347-4727

Region V
(IL, IN, MI, MN, OH, WI)
230 South Dearborn Street
Chicago, IL 60604
Telephone: (312) 353-2000

Region VI
(AR, LA, NM, OK, TX)
1445 Ross Avenue
12th Floor, Suite 1200
Dallas, TX 75270
Telephone: (214) 655-6444

Region VII
(IA, KS, MO, NE)
726 Minnesota Avenue
Kansas City, KS 66101
Telephone: (913) 236-2800

Region VIII
(CO, MT, ND, SD, UT, WY)
999 18th Street, Suite 500
Denver, CO 80202
Telephone: (303) 293-1603

Region IX
(American Samoa, AZ, CA, Guam,
HI, NV, Pacific Tr.Terr.)
215 Fremont Street
San Franciso, CA 94105
Telephone: (415) 974-8071

Region X
(AK, ID, OR, WA)
1200 Sixth Avenue
Seattle, WA 98101
Telephone: (206) 442-5810

Table III

**National Institute for Occupational
Safety and Health Laboratories**

Appalachian Laboratory for
Occupational Safety and Health
944 Chestnut Ridge Road
Morgantown, WV 36505
(304) 291-4126

Robert A. Taft Laboratories
4676 Columbia Parkway
Cincinnati, OH 45226
(513) 533-8236

Appendix VII
Facilities Safety and Housekeeping Inspection Report

This listing is not intended to be complete. Use it as a guide when preparing a similar list for your use that applies to your situation.

Facility No. _____ Bldg. _____

Areas of Inspection	Comments and Recommendations*
1. Bench tops	_____
2. Areas under sinks	_____
3. Cabinets, drawers, shelves (chemicals properly stored)	_____
4. Hoods and other ventilation	_____
5. Aisles	_____
6. Window ledges	_____
7. Walls and floors	_____
8. Chairs, stools, upholstery, casters	_____
9. Safety glasses, face shields, protective clothing	_____
10. Fire extinguishers	_____
11. Compressed gas cylinders	_____
12. Broken glassware: destroy? repair?	_____
13. "No Smoking" and "No Eating" signs	_____
14. Tubing and hoses: condition? proper use?	_____
15. Guards on moving equipment	_____
16. Interlocks	_____
17. Condition of equipment	_____
18. Refrigerators	_____
19. Electric cords, other wiring	_____
20. Eye washes and safety showers	_____
21. Storage of peroxide-forming chemicals	_____
22. Storage of chemicals in work area	_____
23. Storage of chemicals in storage area	_____
24. Evaluation of amount of supplies and equipment	_____
25. Laboratory desks, bookshelves	_____
26. Office housekeeping	_____
27. Other	_____

Actions taken and other recommendations: _____

_____

Inspection made by _____ Date: _____

*Please use additional sheets if necessary.

Index